Deadly Deviates

DEADLY DEVIATES

John Dunning

MULBERRY EDITIONS

To our friends
Fernand and Andrée Hoffman

First published in 1986

Copyright © 1986 John Dunning

This edition published in 1993 for
Mulberry Editions by Cresset Press,
an imprint of Random House UK Limited,
20 Vauxhall Bridge Road, London SW1V 2SA

ISBN 1–873123–43–4

Printed and bound in Great Britain

CONTENTS

INTRODUCTION

Why should I kill thee? Let me count the motives. There . are not really so very many.

Very often it is sexual jealousy. Husband takes girl friend or, in these sexually liberated days, boy friend and is butchered by outraged wife.

More frequently, it is the reverse. Or it can be that boy or girl friend decides to eliminate a disturbing element in an otherwise meaningful relationship.

The various persons involved need not, of course, be formally married either before God or Government.

Murders for gain are not as common as might be thought and, when they do occur, they are more often than not unintentional. Persons with money on their minds want to be out of jail to spend it.

As a matter of fact, most homicides are unintentional. The murderer was in a frenzy of rage, fear or lust, or was befuddled by alcohol or narcotics and, upon regaining his wits, found with astonishment and dismay that he had put an end to someone. This happens rather more often with men than with women, who are more deliberate and less hysterical in such matters.

Jealousy, money, overpowering emotions and, finally, the most terrifying motive of all because it can be neither understood nor predicted: deviation. When there is a dangerous malfunction in the mind of the individual.

Legal and penal authorities in many countries today believe that such malfunctions are subject to treatment and cure and, in some cases, they undoubtedly are.

The difficulty lies in that it is not always possible to determine which cases are cured or curable and errors fatal to innocent persons – tragically, many of them children – occur with monotonous regularity.

It is rare for anyone to be held responsible for these errors. Modern political and social systems are so constructed as to make the authors of decisions as anonymous as possible. Although there is great to-do about rights and privileges, little mention is made of responsibility.

It is a curious manifestation of our times that psychologists, penologists and social workers often have the power to reverse the findings of a court and release into society individuals who prove all too often to be not as harmless as was believed.

Capital punishment has been abolished in most countries, against the will of the majority, if the polls can be believed, and prison sentences become increasingly shorter with regard to actual time served. Real life sentences are reserved for persons who have robbed banks or swindled insurance companies. Murderers and rapists, even if their victims are children, are regarded as suffering from a minor illness which sympathy and a little treatment will cure.

The results of this policy are a brisk coming and going in the psychiatric institutions, with many regular customers, and a dismaying number of victims of rape and murder who would have escaped these fates had the penalties prescribed by law been carried out without interference.

The fact is, psychology is an inexact science and, until such time as it is possible to look inside the brain of the individual and determine precisely not only what he is thinking now, but what he will be thinking six months from now, no person should have the right to release a person convicted of acts of violence until the full sentence has been served or the case has been retried. There is little point in courts handing down heavy sentences if they are to be set aside six months later by persons required to take no responsibility for their acts.

This does not mean that every person sentenced to life imprisonment should die in prison. It means that, if they are released, the decision should be made by persons whose responsibility can be clearly fixed and who will suffer penalties in case of error. Such responsibility might result in the application of more common sense and less ideological dogma.

Current ideology within those circles having to do with the detention of criminals appears to be that there is no such thing as a criminal. Men rape because their mothers were cruel to them. Men murder because of the inequalities of the social and economic systems. The criminal is the victim. The victim is, if anything, an inconvenience to be ignored and forgotten as quickly as possible. Anybody is a criminal. Nobody is a criminal.

In a sense, there is something to this idea. Anyone is a criminal to the extent that anyone is capable of killing. If the human had not been capable of killing in the interests of self or kin, the species could scarcely have survived. Killing has been a part of our biological heritage for a few million years and it is not about to be changed in one or two generations by ideology or anything else. The mills of evolutionary change grind slowly and, in a few hundred thousand years, we may expect to achieve the non-violent human. Assuming that non-violence is a survival factor.

This is, however, what might be termed normal killing, and what we are here concerned with is not murder committed in self-defence or the defence of others, but murders and other acts of violence committed because of a malfunctioning of the perpetrator's mind.

These show considerable variety and not all of them are cases where there is a danger to the general public. Homosexual murders, although the participants may be not entirely within the mainstream of sexual activity, are often not criminal deviations at all, but simple acts of jealousy. On the other hand, the rape or murder of a small child always is, and no person convicted of such an offence should ever be released into society. It is often overlooked today that the primary purpose of government is not redistribution of wealth or the reinsertion of felons into society, but the maintenance of public safety and the protection of the citizen from danger, internal or external.

In the cases dealt with here, there are some which are not truly deviate, which simply means something outside the generally accepted limits of the normal or average, and a good many which are. A few defy description.

This is about what might be expected from humans in general. We are complex beings, far from perfectly constructed, and a lot of things can go wrong.

As many of us have already noticed, when things can go wrong, they usually do.

GOOD NIGHT, NURSE

Standing in front of the door of the two-room apartment on the sixth floor of the building of which he was superintendent, Adrian Martens placed his finger on the button of the doorbell and left it there.

He was annoyed and impatient. He had other things to do and he did not feel that pulling nurses out of bed when they overslept was part of his job.

The apartment building was only four hundred metres from the hospital at 10 Avenue Monseigneur Weyenbergh and a large number of his tenants were nurses and other hospital personnel. Sometimes they overslept, and then the hospital would call – as they had this morning – and he would have to go up and ring the doorbell. They were always apologetic and grateful, but that did not compensate for lost time.

This one seemed to be a stubborn case. There was no response to the doorbell and none to his hammering on the door. Sighing, Martens went back down to the ground-floor office to fetch the pass key. It was beginning to look as if Miss Lutgarde Meeus had flown the coop.

Even hospital nurses sometimes cleared off without notice, but no sooner had he opened the door than he saw that this was something different. The apartment was a shambles, furniture knocked over, rugs kicked into a heap and, draped over the sofa, lay a pair of torn stockings, some ripped underwear and white strips of what looked like a nurse's uniform.

'Miss Meeus?' said Martens tentatively, his throat suddenly dry.

He took two steps into the living room and his gaze passed through the open bathroom door to fix on a fantastic sight.

What looked like the bottom half of a naked woman was leaning against the side of the tub. Her legs, slightly flexed and parted appeared to be broken for they were bent in the wrong direction.

'Miss Meeus!' yelled Martens, losing control of his voice and his nerves simultaneously. He was not a particularly nervous man, but the sight was shocking and totally unexpected.

Although he later had no recollection of it, he was crossing the room as he cried out and, arriving at the bathroom door, saw that what he had taken for a half woman was a whole one draped over the side of the bathtub, her head and shoulders submerged beneath the water with which it was filled. Horribly, the water was a deep red.

Under the shock of the discovery, Martens forgot about the indications of violence in the living room and jumped to the conclusion that Lutgarde Meeus had committed suicide.

Running out of the apartment, he tumbled down the stairs, too excited to think of the elevator, and telephoned the hospital. Their nurse, he gasped, had committed suicide in his building.

As he was extremely excited and out of breath from his run down the stairs, he was not very coherent. The switchboard operator at the hospital did, however, get the idea that something terrible had happened and, within minutes, nurses, interns and other hospital employees were sprinting for the apartment building. Pretty, twenty-eight-year-old Lutgarde had been popular with her colleagues.

'Had been' was the correct tense. It did not take medically trained persons to determine that Lutgarde was dead and had been dead for some time.

Even so, the duty doctor in the emergency room was summoned, but all that he could do was to confirm what they all knew; Lutgarde had been murdered.

In the meantime, Martens had recovered his wits sufficiently to call the police and a patrol car soon arrived.

The officers did nothing, however, other than to look at the corpse, chase the hospital personnel out of the apartment and contact headquarters over the car's radio telephone. The case was clearly homicide and the rest was up to the department of criminal investigations.

What next arrived was, therefore, the duty homicide squad of the Louvain police.

Louvain has a population of less than ninety thousand, but it is only ten miles to the east of Brussels and there is enough contagion from the Belgian capital to make more than one homicide squad necessary.

The one on duty this Wednesday morning of 29 September 1982 consisted of Inspector Karl Groot, a large, smooth-skinned, pink-and-white sort of man with somewhat scanty light brown hair; Sergeant of Detectives Jean Lutgens, who was tall, dark, sallow and rather lugubrious-looking; and a round-faced, cheerful little man who habitually wore his horn-rimmed glasses pushed up on his forehead because he could not see anything through them. This was Dr Bernard Rykers, an expert in forensic medicine and a very good one.

The corpse being in an excellent posture for carrying out a gynaecological examination, the doctor began with that, determining that Miss Meeus had been raped despite desperate resistance. There were lesions of the interior walls of the vagina, hair cuts on the external genitals and the typical black and blue bruise marks on the insides of the thighs caused by the victim clamping her legs over her assailant's hip bones in a vain effort to

3

prevent penetration. The rapist had orgasmed and there was semen in the vaginal passage.

The time of death he estimated as at least twelve hours earlier, making it prior to ten o'clock of the preceding evening. A more precise time would be established during the course of the autopsy.

As for the cause of death, he was unable to say anything until the body had been removed from the bathtub. There was too much blood in the water for any injuries to the head to be seen.

The body could not, as yet, be removed from the bathtub, for the inspector wanted it photographed as it had been found and the laboratory technicians, now on their way, would prefer to carry out their search for potential clues before anything at the scene had been disturbed.

The precaution was routine, but, in this case, unnecessary. Despite an intensive examination of the apartment, nothing was found which could be positively identified as having any connection to either the murder or the murderer. Insofar as could be determined, he had been let into the apartment by Miss Meeus herself. There were no signs of a forced entry.

Nor were there any signs of entertainment: no dirty glasses or cups, no remains of food, no cigarette butts, and the bed in the bedroom had not been slept in.

The most probable course of events was that someone had rung the doorbell at around ten o'clock the preceding evening. Miss Meeus had opened the door and immediately been attacked and overpowered by the intruder before she had time to call for help.

He had presumably left immediately following the murder. There were no indications that he had been in any part of the apartment other than the living room and the bathroom. He had not looked for money or valuables, and Miss Meeus' handbag, lying in full view in the living room, had not been touched.

The inspector's conclusion was that he was dealing

4

with a compulsive sex criminal, a deviate whose only motive was rape and, possibly, murder. He did not think Lutgarde Meeus had been killed to prevent her from identifying her attacker. It was probable she had never laid eyes on him before in her life.

Not so he. The inspector knew a good deal about such sex deviates and he knew they often spent days or even weeks in stalking their proposed victims, following them discreetly in the streets, waiting outside their homes or places of work and searching patiently for a time and place suitable for the kill.

The autopsy showed this time to be earlier than Dr Rykers had thought. His estimate now was between six and six-thirty in the evening of 28 September.

According to other sources of information, this would have been very shortly after Lutgarde had returned home. She had gone off duty at the hospital at five and then done a little shopping for groceries in the neighbourhood stores where she was known. The last reported sighting was at approximately ten minutes to six. She had been wearing her nurse's uniform. This detail was noted, but its significance was not then realized.

It was this uniform which lay in shreds in the living rooms. It had been torn from her body with immense force – a point which Dr Rykers emphasized in the autopsy report.

The murderer, he wrote, was enormously strong and he had huge hands. They had literally crushed Lutgarde Meeus' throat, fracturing the hyoid bone and rupturing the larynx. It was blood from her throat and lungs which had coloured the water in the tub, but there had not been as much of it as appeared.

Otherwise, there were no injuries to the body other than bruises which had been incurred in Lutgarde's struggle with the rapist. She had apparently not managed to mark him for there were no traces of skin or hair beneath her fingernails.

Dr Rykers thought the struggle had been of short

duration and the strangulation was, perhaps, necessary for the deviate to achieve his sexual climax so that rape and murder had taken place almost simultaneously. He stated flatly in his report that the murderer was sexually abnormal and that it was unlikely that this was his first offence. There was, in all probability, a file on him in the police records, but, as no clues to his identity had been found at the scene, there was no way of knowing which one it was. Unfortunately, the killer had no marked idiosyncrasy, as did some sex criminals, which could serve as a sort of trademark.

Actually, the killer did; but at the time no one realized it.

Inspector Groot therefore proceeded with the customary routine of the investigation, checking out the backgrounds and, in so far as possible, the whereabouts on the evening of 28 September of every male with whom Lutgarde had had contact – and found nothing.

Granted that the murder was almost certainly a deviate sex crime, the question remained of why Lutgarde had let a stranger into her apartment. There was, of course, always the possibility of a simulated sex crime, although it was rare for one to be so cleverly imitated as this.

Postmen, dustmen, power, gas and telephone company personnel were traced, not only the bona fide service men, but also possible impostors. People who would never have dreamed of letting a stranger into their apartments freely opened their doors to men wearing the uniform of one of the public services.

Again, the results were negative. No public service men of any kind had been seen in the building on the day in question and the building superintendent, Martens, swore that none could have entered without his knowledge.

Just after taking Martens' statement concerning the service men, when Sergeant Lutgens was passing out through the main entrance hall in a not too cheerful mood – he had put in a great deal of effort on the case and, so far, had got nowhere – he saw ambling towards him a tall, strongly built man with a clean-cut, boyish face and a bashful expression. The young man was dressed in the white overalls and jacket of a house painter and was carrying a bucket of paint and some brushes.

The sergeant stopped him. 'Who,' he said, 'are you?'

The young man, who turned out to be not as young as he looked, said that his name was Michel Bellen and added, rather unnecessarily, that he was a house painter employed by a firm contracted to repaint some of the apartments in the building.

The sergeant looked thoughtfully at Bellen's hands, which were the size of banjos, identified himself as a police officer and asked to see his papers.

Bellen produced them. He was, it seemed, thirty-six years old, unmarried and had been born in Antwerp, thirty-five miles to the north. There was a restriction in the personal identity card to the effect that it was not valid for residence in Antwerp.

'Why?' demanded the sergeant, the hair on his neck beginning to rise. He knew of only one reason in Belgium why a man could not legally reside in the city of his birth.

'I was given the death sentence,' said Bellen in a low, embarrassed voice, looking at the floor.

That was the reason.

'For what?' said the sergeant, reaching for his hand-cuffs and his service pistol.

'Killing nurses,' said Michel Bellen shyly.

And that was the end of the case. Michel Bellen was none other than the notorious Killer of the Left Bank who, eighteen years earlier, had frightened the women of Antwerp nearly out of their wits, had raped three and killed two of them, had been described by the medical experts at his trial as a dangerous psychopath who could never be allowed to mingle with the public and had been condemned to death, a verdict which received the approval of nearly everyone, not excluding the defendant.

The whole process – murders, rapes, trial and sentencing – took place during less than thirteen months. It began four days before Sunday, 9 August 1964, when two elderly ladies taking a stroll on the Left Bank of the Schelde, the river which runs through Antwerp, a city of some 200,000 inhabitants, discovered the body of twenty-eight-year-old Lucienne Verhoeven, a professional nurse, lying among the bushes.

The young woman was a terrible sight for she had been strangled with such force that her eyes started from her head, her tongue protruded black and swollen from her mouth and the skin of her face turned slate blue.

She was totally naked, even her shoes having been removed, and the torn shreds of her nurse's uniform lay around her.

Even to two elderly ladies unaccustomed to such sights, it was obvious that she had been raped, for she lay as her murderer had risen from her, on her back, with sprawled thighs, her arms bent at the elbows in the last dying effort to tear the strangling hands from her throat.

It being August, there were many insects and, as the body had been lying there since the preceding Wednesday, it had been visited by birds and small animals.

One of the ladies immediately and understandably fainted and was nearly murdered herself by her companion who, terrified at being left alone with a corpse and an unconscious woman, shook her so violently that she later required medical attention.

The second lady being thus roused, both made off as fast as possible to report their discovery to the police. This took a little time as most of Antwerp is on the Right Bank and the Left Bank has few buildings and, consequently, few telephones.

Even when the police had finally been notified and

hurried to the scene, there was not a great deal that they could do other than identify the victim.

Miss Verhoeven had been reported missing on Thursday morning by her colleagues at the hospital, but there was no certainty of the exact time of her disappearance. Nor was there now any explanation as to what she had been doing on the Left Bank. The hospital was, of course, on the Right Bank, as was the apartment building in which she lived.

The case was assigned to a team of investigators headed by Inspector Jan Dykstra, a man who curiously resembled Inspector Groot in Louvain, who would be investigating a similar case eighteen years later. He was, of course, considerably older. When Lucienne Verhoeven was murdered, Inspector Groot was still a detective first class and only beginning his career. By the time of the Lutgarde Meeus murder, Inspector Dykstra was already retired.

Assisting Inspector Dykstra was a sergeant of detectives named Piet Haan, a very handsome young man who would later leave the police to make a successful career as an actor in television plays in which he almost invariably played the role of a clever crook.

These two, and a rather sinister-looking medical expert with a sharp, pointed moustache and a small, sharp beard, who was called Leopold Bulcke and was actually a very mild sort of person and a devoted family man, formed the nucleus of the detachment investigating what soon came to be known as the Murders of the Left Bank.

Having failed to discover anything of significance at the scene – other than the fact that it really was the scene of the murder and not merely the place where the killer had disposed of the body – the corpse was transferred to the police morgue, where Dr Bulcke carried out an autopsy of it.

In his report, the doctor stated that Miss Verhoeven

9

had been strangled by someone with enormously strong hands who had raped her simultaneously or nearly so.

The sexual frenzy of the rapist had been such that he had shown no more consideration for his own genitals than for those of his victim. He had cut himself rather badly for there was a quantity of blood of a different group than Miss Verhoeven's in her pubic hair. There was reason to believe that he had achieved orgasm, although any semen present had, by this time, broken down chemically.

There were no indications of resistance by Miss Verhoeven, who had, perhaps, hoped to save her life through cooperation.

She had lost it on the evening of 5 August some time after six in the evening and earlier than midnight. Due to the length of time before discovery of the body, he was unable to be more precise.

The doctor was of the opinion that the murderer was a compulsive sex psychopath who had no control whatsoever over his own actions and who, if he had not already committed such crimes in the past, could be counted upon to commit more of them in the future.

Although Inspector Dykstra did not care at all for this prophecy, it turned out to be accurate and, on 30 August, there was a repetition of the Verhoeven murder, as similar as the murderer could make it.

The similarity had a reason. The Killer of the Left Bank could obtain sexual satisfaction only through a specific combination of circumstances, those present at the rape and murder of Lucienne Verhoeven.

It was necessary that the victim be female, attractive, in her middle or late twenties and, above all, that she be wearing a nurse's uniform or something that looked like it.

Later, there would be reason to believe that the victim also had to possess a negative attribute. She could not be a mother.

Had the women of Antwerp known what was in

Michel Bellen's mind, they could have assured their safety simply by eschewing nurses' uniforms or laying claim, whether truthfully or otherwise, to motherhood.

But, of course, no one knew that Michel Bellen was the Killer of the Left Bank and, even when it was known, the psychologists were never in complete agreement as to what went on inside that physically attractive but dangerously aberrant head.

They did agree on one thing. Bellen was a menace to certain women and there was no reason to believe he would ever be otherwise. If he were not removed permanently from society, he would kill again.

Not, of course, that he wanted to. Michel Bellen was a gentle, shy and unassuming youth who would grow into a gentle, shy and unassuming man. He was kind, thoughtful and had a pleasant personality. There was not a thing wrong with him except that the greatest ecstasy of which he was capable was the rape and murder of a woman wearing a nurse's uniform.

It was the second murder, on the afternoon or evening of Sunday, 30 August, which gained Bellen his nickname of the Killer of the Left Bank and Inspector Dykstra a reputation within the department for perspicacity.

Twenty-seven-year-old Christiane Herreman was approximately the age of Lucienne Verhoeven. She was pretty. And she was a nurse. When she failed to report for work on Monday morning, some of her colleagues went to her apartment and, finding no trace of her there, called the police. They were still nervous over what had happened to Lucienne Verhoeven earlier that same month and they were aware that the murderer had not been identified.

The police were equally nervous and Inspector Dykstra ran a quick check of all the places that Miss Herreman might be and then ordered a search of the Left Bank. There were so many other parallels to the

Verhoeven case that he thought there might be another in the scene of the crime.

His reasoning was faultless. Christiane Herreman's body was discovered less than a hundred yards from the place where Lucienne Verhoeven had been murdered, and the only real differences in the two cases were the dates and the identities of the victims.

Miss Herreman had been stripped naked, strangled with terrifying force and brutally raped. Not as much time had elapsed before the discovery of the body as in the Verhoeven murder, so Dr Bulcke was able to establish the time of death as approximately six-thirty in the evening of 30 August within half an hour in either direction.

The information was of little use to the investigation, but the doctor was unable to provide anything else and the technicians from the police laboratory who went over the scene literally with magnifying glasses were no more successful. Bellen had completed another perfect murder under the noses of the police.

And, in fact, there is no telling how many such perfect crimes Michel Bellen might have committed had he stuck strictly to rape and murder. In these fields he was practically undetectable, aside from sheer bad luck such as someone stumbling on him while he was actually engaged in the crime.

That was, however, unlikely for Bellen did not take very long with his work. Rape and murder took place nearly simultaneously and he was always in such a state of excitement that penetration was followed by orgasm within seconds.

Neither did the murder last very long. The victim scarcely had time to realize that there was something wrong with this attractive but shy young man when their clothing was ripped away and the huge, deadly hands locked round their throats. The pressure was such that not only air to the lungs but the blood supply to the

12

brain was cut off instantly and unconsciousness followed within less than a minute.

It was later estimated that the attack took less than five minutes and, if Bellen were not disturbed during this short time, there was little hope of apprehending him. He never had any prior contact with his victims, other than having seen them wearing their nurse's uniforms, and he never left any traces of his identity at the scene, other than his semen and a little blood. His blood group was a valueless indication: it was the same as roughly a quarter of the population of Belgium.

The Killer of the Left Bank might have continued his career for some time, had he not been so discriminating in his choice of victims, but he could not, of course, help this any more than he could help raping and murdering nurses.

As a result, on 16 August, precisely two weeks before the murder of Christiane Herreman, he had already sown the seeds of his own destruction.

The direct cause of Michel Bellen's downfall was an attractive young woman named Josette Mauberge. At twenty-nine, she was one year older than the oldest of his other victims, but she looked, if anything, younger.

Although Bellen had no way of knowing this, she was not acceptable prey at all as she was not a nurse, but only a nurse's helper at the hospital. Deceptively, she wore a uniform which might easily be confused with that of a nurse.

Finally and, for Bellen, unfortunately, Josette Mauberge was not only a mother, but a fourfold one to boot. She did not, however, have a husband as she was divorced.

Not celibate and far less discriminating than Bellen, she was not at all reluctant to accept a ride on his motor scooter from this handsome, engagingly bashful young stranger. Nor did she raise any objection when, instead

13

of taking her home, he crossed the bridge spanning the Schelde to the secluded Left Bank.

As she later admitted, it had not been the most prudent thing in the world to do. Like everyone else in Antwerp, she had read of the murder of Lucienne Verhoeven, but it did not occur to her to associate it with this handsome stranger.

Arriving at a suitably private spot, the driver parked the scooter and seized Josette Mauberge in a grip of iron.

Josette took this for passion and, indeed, it was, but of a different kind than she could possibly imagine.

Holding her helpless with one hand, he tore away her clothing with the ease of a man plucking a chicken. He was so enormously strong that Josette, a healthy and far from feeble young woman, could do nothing other than protest that he was ruining her things and that, if he would wait a minute, she would take them off herself.

The man paid no attention to her, seemed not even to hear her. To Josette's alarm, he appeared to be having a sort of fit, his eyes glaring wildly and his mouth slightly open and drooling saliva. He did not look like the attractive stranger from whom she had accepted a ride less than twenty minutes earlier.

Flinging his naked victim violently to the ground, the Killer of the Left Bank parted her legs with his hands and entered her to the hilt, orgasming almost instantly.

This was not Josette's idea of romantic love-making, but she was no longer concerned with that. The penetration without preparation had been painful and she had now recalled Lucienne Verhoeven and what had happened to her on the Left Bank of the Schelde.

She did not have much time to think about it for, even as he penetrated her, the killer had laid his hands about her throat.

In that terrible instant when Josette Mauberge realized that her death was only seconds away, her maternal instincts overrode her own fear.

'I have four children!' she screamed.

The greatest magician in the world could not have pronounced a more efficacious formula. Bellen removed his hands from her throat, got to his feet, zipped up his trousers, shot her an embarrassed look, climbed on to his motor scooter and roared away without a word.

Mrs Mauberge lay on the ground trying to decide whether she was going to become hysterical or not. Her throat hurt a little and her private parts hurt a great deal, but she was basically unharmed.

After a time, she decided that she was not going to have hysterics, got up, managed to assemble enough of her clothing for decency and set off home at a brisk pace. It had occurred to her that the man might change his mind and come back. She had no way of knowing that her motherhood was more protection than a squad of armed bodyguards.

Mrs Mauberge did not go to the police to report her experience. If she had, she might have saved the life of Christiane Herreman, although not that of Lutgarde Meeus.

She did not go to the police for the same reason that many victims of rape do not. The ordeal of testifying before a court and a hostile defence counsel can seem as bad as the rape.

Moreover, her position was not strong. She would have to admit that she had let a total stranger drive her over to the bushes of the Left Bank and she could scarcely claim that it had been to pick wild flowers. Any self-respecting defence counsel would have little trouble convincing a court that she had practically invited rape, if not insisted upon it.

Josette did, however, have an uneasy feeling about the matter and she did realize that the man on the scooter might very well have been the murderer of Lucienne Verhoeven.

She turned the events over in her mind a good deal and, when Christiane Herreman's death was announced in the newspapers, she not only went to the police, but she had a substantial amount of useful information to give them, including a remarkably exact description of the young man and his motor scooter.

The motor scooter proved to be more easily spotted than the man. Inspector Dykstra had posted plainclothes officers at all of the city's hospitals on the theory that the Killer of the Left Bank was apparently obsessed with medical personnel, and Bellen was soon taken into custody.

Fortunately for the investigators and for the women of Antwerp, he proved to be cooperative. Although the police still had no evidence against him, other than a possible identification by Josette Mauberge which would have sustained nothing more than a charge of rape and probably not that, Bellen promptly confessed.

Yes, he said, he had killed two nurses and raped another. He did not know why. There was something about a nurse's uniform which excited him terribly so that he did not know what he was doing. He was very sorry. He hoped the authorities would do something to stop him.

The authorities would do something, but not enough. Bellen was examined by the country's leading psychologists and psychiatrists, who were unable to agree on anything other than that Bellen was dangerous.

The only thing unusual in his background was that he had suffered a head injury in his early teens and his personality had apparently changed following this. He had run away from home three or four times and had been caught stealing on several occasions. His parents, unable to control him, had asked that he be made a ward of the juvenile court and he had been under the court's control up to the age of eighteen. He had murdered Lucienne Verhoeven less than a year later.

It was not only the psychologists who maintained that Bellen was dangerous and that he would kill again, given the opportunity. So too did Bellen, and the court handed down the death penalty.

Belgium, however, was in the peculiar position of having the death penalty under law, but never carrying it out.

Bellen was sentenced to death on 24 September 1965. It was commuted to life imprisonment on 1 December of that same year.

Eighteen years later, on 3 May 1982, the penal authorities decided that Bellen had been in jail long enough and released him. He was carefully reinserted into society, found an apartment and a job, and supported financially until such time as he could support himself. Neither his employers nor anyone else in Louvain knew of his criminal record, not even the police.

On 27 September 1982, he saw Lutgarde Meeus in the apartment house where he was painting. She was wearing her uniform.

On 28 September, he killed her.

On 25 November 1983, Michel Bellen was sentenced to death for raping and murdering his third nurse.

Belgium still does not carry out the death penalty.

On 12 May 1984, Bellen's sentence was commuted to life imprisonment.

And?

2

ROMEO WORE LIPSTICK

The minute hand of the big clock on the charge room wall moved forward a click to midnight and, in that instant, the telephone on the duty sergeant's desk rang.

The sergeant, two hours into the night shift, put down his magazine and lifted the receiver. The caller was the dispatcher in the communications centre on the floor above.

'Reported shooting at the corner of Theresien and Luisen Strassen,' said the dispatcher. 'I've got two cars on the way. Give you a direct report as soon as they're at the scene.'

'Understood,' said the desk sergeant and broke the connection so that he could dial the number of the department of criminal investigations. If this was not a practical joke or an alcohol or drug-induced fantasy, somebody would have to go out.

Practical jokes and fantasies were both common enough on the night-shift in the Schwabing sub-station of the Munich police. The district had once been an artists' quarter and the people who now lived there thought that they were artists, which meant that they were high on something most of the time. And, consequently, they not infrequently assaulted or murdered each other.

The sergeant informed the young detective second class who answered the telephone that there was a shooting report awaiting confirmation and got out a first information report form, which he filled in with the date,

8 July 1976. Wednesday, the seventh, was obviously when the crime had taken place, if it had at all, but his first information had been received on the eighth.

Six minutes later, the telephone rang again. It was an officer from one of the patrol cars at the scene, reporting directly over the communications desk.

'Taxi,' said the officer laconically. 'Two women in front seat either unconscious or dead. Some blood. Looks like gunshot wounds. Instructions?'

'Remain at scene until arrival of CID,' said the sergeant automatically. 'Hold any persons present. Prevent unauthorized persons from approaching vehicle.'

He broke the connection and dialled the number of the criminal investigations department. 'Confirmed shooting at Theresien and Luisen,' he said. 'It's all yours. You can pick up the FIR on your way out.'

His part in the matter was now complete. The detectives assigned to the case would pick up the first information report and fill in the details. The dispatcher would already have sent an ambulance to the scene. A routine case for the night desk. The sergeant put his heels back up on the bottom drawer of the desk and resumed his reading of a detective magazine.

In the department of criminal investigations, Inspector Walter Schreiber, duty officer in charge of the shift, was preparing to answer the call personally under the sulky gaze of his assistant, Sergeant of Detectives Max Kaufmann.

The inspector looked smug. He was a man of faintly noble appearance, with a prominent chin and long, blond hair which looked as if it was artificially waved but was not.

The sergeant was sulky because it was not he who was going out. Like many plain-clothes officers, he did not like being cooped up in an office, particularly on a warm summer night, and he felt that the outside investigation work should be left to people who were not drawing an inspector's salary to sit in offices and take charge of things.

However, the inspector was in charge, so if he wanted to go out, go out he did. He soon disappeared, leaving his grumbling subordinate in charge in his absence.

Fortunately for the sergeant's opinion of his chief and police organization in general, his confinement to the office did not last long. In something less than twenty minutes, the inspector called over the radio-telephone.

'I need you out here, Max,' he said. 'Put Willi in charge and come on out, but before you do, call headquarters and tell them we've got a double homicide and we need a car taken in to the garage for examination. They'll have to bring in some of the lab people to go over it. It's not clear what happened, but I think it was a bungled hold-up. I can't find the money bag, and this is a cab.'

'Did a call go out?' said the sergeant anxiously.

The question was one to make any police officer anxious. Munich, the biggest city in the south of West Germany, has a population of over a million and a half, which means that there is a good deal of violent crime and not a little of it involves taxi drivers or prostitutes.

The reason is the same in both cases. Both professions require picking up total strangers and taking them to often secluded places where money changes hands.

In the case of the taxi driver, at least, this means that he has to carry a substantial amount of change on him. Here he is at a disadvantage to the prostitute, who normally carries no change and immediately hands her earnings over to her pimp or seals them into a self-addressed envelope to be dropped into the nearest post box.

Prostitution is, therefore, slightly less risky than driving a cab, but neither is safe when some junkie, desperate for a fix, ponders the possibility of obtaining one through dynamic use of a switchblade.

Prostitutes respond to this threat by keeping pimps

20

handy, or large attack dogs, which are cheaper. Taxi drivers seek to defend themselves with a length of lead pipe under the seat or a pair of brass knuckles. A few carry guns, but not legally. In modern civilized countries such as West Germany, the government does not permit its citizens to protect themselves, whether it is capable of protecting them or not.

However, in compensation for the greater risk, taxi drivers have opportunity for dissuasion not available to prostitutes. Their cabs are equipped with radio-telephones and, in an emergency, the dispatchers at the various company offices can tie the entire fleet into a single network.

An attack on a taxi driver is regarded as an emergency and, as the circuit is almost always open, the dispatcher hears what is going on even if the driver has no time or breath to call for help.

What happens then is frightening. All over the city, cabs brake, swing around and go roaring in toward the location of the distress call. The effect is a little like a horror film of the future with robot cars gone mad and moving in for the kill.

And, as a matter of fact, that is precisely what the drivers have in mind. If they catch the culprit, they not infrequently beat him to death, particularly if the attack has ended fatally for the driver.

It was this possibility which alarmed Sergeant Kaufmann, not because he was personally averse to the lynching of murdering hopheads, but because such an operation invariably resulted in a messy case for the police, involving a great deal of work which could end with what he regarded as an unjust solution.

Dozens of uncooperative cab drivers would have to be interrogated, endless deliberately deceptive stories would have to be checked and, if the case was finally solved, some honest, hard-working cabbie would go to jail for having executed a killer who should long since have been executed by the government.

To the sergeant's relief, the inspector replied that apparently no call had gone out as there were no taxis at the scene other than the one in which the shooting had taken place.

The driver of this cab had been one of the two women shot, for it was her picture on the licence posted on the back of the seat.

It was a good picture of a good subject. Women taxi drivers were not unusual by any means, but it was not often that they were as attractive as this one. According to Inspector Schreiber, who had arrived just as the bodies were being loaded into the ambulance, she was maddeningly beautiful with long, silky blonde hair and a figure to bring tears to a man's eyes. She had been, he added, practically naked.

The sergeant did not believe this. He was a rather skinny, sallow young man with protruding front teeth and his hair falling over his eyes and he was very serious about nearly everything.

The inspector, who had been in criminal investigations too long to be serious about anything and risk his sanity, was inclined to torture him in various mild ways as he thought it good for the development of his character. This caused the sergeant to regard with suspicion such stories of having just missed seeing an improbably beautiful half-naked victim.

Who, it seemed, was perhaps not a victim at all or, at least, not a homicide victim. Despite the inspector's report concerning a double homicide, neither woman had been dead at the time that she had been loaded into the ambulance. It was merely that, to the inspector's experienced eye, their chances of survival did not appear good.

However the story about the woman driver being nearly naked was true. The other woman had been not far from it, either. What this meant, the inspector had no idea.

He had no idea what had happened at all, other than

that both driver and passenger had been in the front seat, the motor had been turned off at the time of the shooting and the money bag was missing.

According to the licence, the driver's name was Eleonore Bele and she was twenty-five years old. Her address was given as 28 Bahnhof Strasse in Unterfoehring, which was a suburb on the north-east edge of the city and not a particularly good one.

There was no indication as to the identity of the passenger, who had either not been carrying a bag or had had it stolen by the murderer.

After a time, a car appeared at the scene and two technicians from the police laboratory got out and went over the area around the cab. It was all clean-swept pavement and they soon came over to report that they had found nothing of any significance.

They then got back into the car and went home. It would be other technicians who would check out the cab once it had been towed to the police garage.

This operation was not something that required supervision by the inspector or the sergeant and they returned resignedly to the office. The sergeant telephoned the emergency hospital and was told that one of the women had been dead on arrival and the other was in critical condition. Both had been shot.

The sergeant then opened a homicide file, leaving the name blank as he had forgotten to ask the hospital which woman was dead. He did not know whether it was Eleonore Bele or the passenger.

The rest of the shift was quiet, with only a few drunken fights resulting in assault charges and one non-fatal knifing in a homosexual bar.

Although the inspector and the sergeant had only come off duty at six in the morning, they were back in the office by noon. They had been on duty at the time the case originated and the policy was to let a homicide team remain with a case they had started.

The first part of the investigation was to find out

whether it was single or double homicide. If the second victim had not died, she might be able to solve the case for them with little or no effort and, at the worst, she could probably provide useful descriptions of the murderer and the circumstances.

To the sergeant's relief, it appeared that the woman who had been dead on arrival at the hospital was not the lovely taxi driver, but the older and less attractive passenger. Her body had already been transferred to the police morgue and was now being autopsied. There was still no clue as to her identity.

Eleonore Bele was alive, but unconscious and still critical. She had been shot twice, once through each breast. The doctors had removed one bullet. The other was still in her, considered too dangerous to remove at the moment.

The sergeant, still on the telephone, conveyed this information to his chief.

'Where was the other woman shot?' asked the inspector.

The sergeant inquired. 'In the crotch,' he said. 'Three bullets.'

'That suggest anything to you?' said the inspector.

'Sex orientated?' said the sergeant. 'Breasts of one. Genitals of the other.'

'Right,' said the inspector. 'Get hold of the records section and see if they can locate a file on a woman named Alster or Albers. There was a case a year or so ago. Girl who specialized in holding up taxi drivers. Not on drugs or anything. She just liked money. Could be under juveniles. She was very young, as I recall.'

'Why her particularly?' said the sergeant, reaching for the telephone again.

'She was a lesbian,' said the inspector.

It turned out that his memory was half good. The name of the girl in question was not Alster or Albers, but Altmeyer, Doris Altmeyer, and the case had not taken place a year or so ago, but nearly four years earlier, when Doris had been barely eighteen. It had, therefore, definitely been a case for the juvenile court.

In other respects, the inspector was more accurate. Doris was a self-acknowledged lesbian who wanted desperately to be a man and who had, more or less, convinced herself that she was one. She was also a specialist in knocking over taxi drivers and had been convicted on no less than five counts of armed robbery.

At the time, Doris had been using a Belgian Fabrique Nationale 7.65 mm automatic pistol and, according to the ballistics experts who examined the bullets extracted from Eleonore Bele and the corpse of the unidentified passenger, they were of the same calibre, although what gun they had been fired from could not be said. It was not Doris's original Belgian FN, for that had been confiscated by the police and was still in the police museum.

If the whereabouts of Doris Altmeyer's gun was known, Doris's were not. Being a juvenile, she had got off with a very light sentence and, as was usually the case, had served only a small fraction of that. She had been released at the beginning of 1975 and was supposed to have reported regularly to a parole officer, but he had not laid eyes on her so much as once.

If the police had thought about it at all, they would have assumed that Doris had gone back to holding up cabs. Most of the convicted felons released early for reintegration into society returned immediately to their original occupations.

The police had not thought about it, however. Nor had anyone else. In a city of a million and a half, Doris was merely a figure in a statistic and not a very important one either. After all, she had never actually murdered anyone.

But it was possible that she had now, and the inspector put the sergeant to hunting for her.

He himself took charge of a smaller detail engaged in trying to identify the passenger who had been killed.

All that Dr Wilfried Tesch, the police medical expert who had carried out the autopsy, was able to tell the inspector concerning the victim was that she had been healthy, in her forties, very well groomed, and possibly homosexual as her pubic area was shaved and she wore a small gold ring in her left labia major. She had never born a child or had a major operation. The immediate cause of death had been a severed femoral artery resulting in massive haemorrhaging. There was some dental work, and charts were provided for submission to dentists throughout the city.

The operation was begun, but proved unnecessary as the inspector's detectives, canvassing the homosexual bars and cafés with pictures of the dead woman, came up with a positive identification first.

As Dr Tesch had surmised, forty-four-year-old Inge Labe had been a lesbian and, as it turned out, a very well known one in some circles. She could not have been identified by her dental work, however, for she was not German. She was Austrian and came from Vienna, where the dental work had been done.

Being a foreign resident, Inge Labe was registered with the Foreign Registrations Office, where the records showed that she was a successful designer of women's clothing and that she lived in Schwabing at 144 Elisabeth Strasse.

A team from the police laboratory went through her apartment and found interesting although not particularly useful evidence of Miss Labe's preferred sexual activities. They also found so many fingerprints left by Eleonore Bele, still in serious condition at the hospital but now expected to recover, that they concluded she had been a very frequent visitor, if not a resident.

For Inspector Schreiber this changed the character of the case completely. He no longer considered money to have been the motive for the shootings and he did not think that Inge Labe had been a passenger in the cab at the time.

26

Rather than murder for robbery, the case was simply a love triangle, perhaps one in which the sexes of the participants were somewhat confused, but basically an emotional crime, the motive for which had been sexual jealousy.

This change in theory made Doris Altmeyer a less promising suspect, but it did not eliminate her altogether. Inge Labe had been killed and Eleonore Bele had been wounded, undoubtedly by a lesbian lover of one or the other. Doris was a lesbian and an attractive one. She could as well have been the jealous lover as anyone else.

She was not, however. This was learned with certainty only a short time later. Sergeant Kaufmann, who had been scouring Munich for her with no success, suddenly got the idea that Doris might have gone elsewhere to get in trouble and sent out a request for information over the police telex.

There was a reply within an hour. Doris had gone to Berlin, a mecca for German homosexuals, and resumed the only profession she knew, that of robbing taxi drivers, and was once again in jail. Questioned later about her views on the Labe murder, she expressed the opinion that the police were not right in the head. She would never, she said firmly, have held up a woman taxi driver. All her targets were men.

According to the police records, Doris was telling the truth concerning her professional practices and, probably, also concerning her opinion of the police. But if the police were not right in the head, it did not say much for her intelligence that they had now managed to send her to jail twice!

However, the inspector was not interested. A suspect had been eliminated and the investigation could move on to the next.

The next suspect was thirty-four-year-old Linda Schnitzler, who was small, dark, elfin, pretty and tough. Like

Eleonore Bele, she was a taxi driver and, like both victims, she was a lesbian.

Eleonore Bele, who had by now recovered sufficiently to be interrogated, said that she did not know her, but police contacts in local homosexual circles said that she not only knew her but had been living with her for years.

The sources also said that Linda had been insanely jealous of Eleonore and had beaten her up on occasion for real or fancied flirtations with other women. This was hard to imagine as Eleonore was half a head taller and twenty pounds heavier than her slight but wiry lover, but it was apparently true.

The police were soon to learn how firm a character Linda Schnitzler was. Having taken her into custody and charged her formally with the shootings, they attempted to interrogate a confession out of her and ran head-on into a small, grim stone wall.

Linda would not admit that she had ever heard the names of Eleonore Bele and Inge Labe. She would not admit that she was a lesbian. She would not even admit that she was a taxi driver, although the licence with her picture on it was in her cab. She would not admit to anything.

This was awkward for the police, but not insurmountable. A search of the apartment at 28 Bahnhof Strasse in Unterfoehring, where both Eleonore and Linda were registered, provided ample evidence that the couple had been living there for years. Both women's clothing was still present, as were all of their personal possessions and papers.

There was, therefore, proof positive that Linda and Eleonore had been living together for some considerable time as woman and wife, and there was evidence that Linda had been jealous. There was, however, no concrete evidence to connect her to the shootings.

No gun had been found in the apartment or in Linda's cab and the police were unable to locate any gunsmith's where a woman answering to Linda's description had purchased a gun. No witnesses had been found. Although it would have been possible to obtain an indictment at this point, without material evidence or a confession the chances of a conviction were slim.

Linda had, by now, convinced the inspector that he was not going to get any confession out of her, so he suspended the interrogation and turned his attention to Eleonore. He estimated Eleonore to be of less stern stuff, and she should know if it was Linda who had shot her.

Eleonore did, but she was reluctant to say. As she was not a suspect, but a victim, the inspector could not apply much pressure.

Instead, he resorted to sympathy, a tactic of which he could make convincing use as he was quite sincerely sympathetic to Eleonore's and Linda's problems. Having a good deal to do with homosexuals in his work, he was aware that their sexual peculiarity often caused them great unhappiness and was the source of much instability in their lives. Both Eleonore and Linda had been confirmed lesbians from early youth and neither had ever had any emotional contact whatsoever with men. Their relationship, sanctioned neither by society nor by any legal or religious bond, had been insecure and Linda, nine years older than her lover, had probably lived in a state of continual fear of losing her.

The sympathy worked to an extent. Eleonore admitted that she and Linda had been living together since May of 1969, when they met in a homosexual bar. It had been love at first sight and they moved in together immediately.

Eleonore also admitted that she was a little flighty and that she had sometimes indulged in flirtations with other women. Linda had beaten her up and she had deserved it. She insisted, however, that she had never actually been unfaithful.

Never, until Inge climbed into her cab on 21 May of that year. Eleonore remembered the date very well. She also remembered what had happened afterwards.

She drove Inge to her apartment in Elisabeth Strasse and was invited up for a drink. She accepted, and was so swept off her feet that she remained for the rest of the night. Inge, she said, was the most fantastic lover she had ever encountered. She was skilled beyond all belief.

Linda had beaten her up for this escapade, but she was unable to resist Inge and went back to the apartment repeatedly. In the end, however, they had to resort to making love in her cab as Linda learned Inge's address and often cruised by to see if Eleonore's cab was parked in the vicinity.

They had been making a little love on the night of 7 July in the cab, parked at the corner of Theresien and Luisen Strassen, when someone came up and shot them through the open window. She had no idea who it might have been.

The inspector replied that this was not true. She knew very well it had been Linda. There was no point in continuing to protect her. She was going to be indicted, tried and convicted.

Eleonore wept and said that she hoped not, but she still would not identify Linda as the murderess.

The inspector withdrew, temporarily defeated. Eleonore was not going to testify against her lover, even if she had shot her.

Even so, the police were now fairly confident of obtaining a conviction on the circumstantial evidence. Linda Schnitzler was brought before the examining magistrate formally indicted on one count of homicide and one count of wounding with a deadly weapon.

Two days later, the police received a frantic telephone call from a woman in Frankfurt who identified herself as Linda Schnitzler's mother. Her daughter, she said, was planning suicide. The police should stop her.

As it is German police policy not to give out any more information than necessary, the officer taking the call did not mention that Linda was in the detention cells awaiting trial and not, therefore, in a position to carry out her suicide plans, but merely transferred the call to Inspector Schreiber's office.

The inspector listened to what Mrs Schnitzler had to say and assured her that her daughter was alive and that he would take steps to prevent her from doing away with herself. He asked how she had come to know of the proposed suicide.

Mrs Schnitzler said that she had received a letter from Linda dated 6 July. She had been away visiting relatives for a few days and had only just returned to find the letter, which she now read to him.

It was short. *'Dear Mama,'* it read, *'Don't be angry. Eleonore has lied to me and deceived me. Bury me at home near you.'*

There was no mention of murder, but, if there were a conviction at the trial, this was evidence of premeditation. Careful not to alarm the woman, the inspector asked if she would send the letter down to him so that a psychologist could look at it. It might be useful in any treatment necessary. He did not mention that the treatment would be a judicial one.

The letter was received two days later. It did not impress either Linda or Eleonore, both of whom stuck to their original stories.

However, while waiting for the trial, which took place on 6 May 1977, Linda Schnitzler changed her mind and confessed to the shootings. She regretted what she had done, she said, but she had simply been unable to live without Eleonore and Inge was stealing her away.

Linda Schnitzler was found guilty on both charges but, despite the evidence of premeditation, was granted extenuating circumstances so that she was sentenced to a modest seven years' imprisonment.

Eleonore said that she would wait.

'What do I put in for the motive?' said Sergeant Kaufmann, filling out the closing case report. 'Deviate sex?'

The inspector looked at him thoughtfully.

'Was it?' he said.

'Was it what?' said the sergeant warily. He was never quite sure how serious the inspector was when he looked thoughtful.

'Deviate sex,' said the inspector. 'Of course, everybody involved in the case was sexually abnormal, but did that have anything to do with the shooting?'

The sergeant said nothing. He did not think that the inspector expected a reply.

'Wasn't Linda's jealousy as normal as that of any lover?' continued the inspector. 'Wasn't Inge's infatuation with Eleonore understandable in a person in her forties confronted with a lush and willing twenty-five-year-old? And wasn't Eleonore's refusal to incriminate the woman who shot her a pure example of the loyalty and devotion of one lover to another?'

He fixed the slightly open-mouthed sergeant with a grave and steady gaze.

'If the sexes had been orthodox, what would you have put down then?'

The sergeant closed his mouth. 'Romeo, Juliet and the Other Guy,' he said.

He typed in 'Deviate sex' and went on to the next entry.

3

DEVILISH ACTIVE, THESE GERMAN KIDS!

'*All those who read this book shall be damned for all eternity*,' read Detective Sergeant Peter Froebes in an emotionless official voice. '*May Our Lord Lucifer drag them down into the hottest fires of Hell.*'

He handed the little plastic-bound diary to Inspector Arnold Deutsch.

'Poorly educated person,' he remarked. 'There are half a dozen grammatical errors in every sentence.'

'Other interests than academic,' grunted the inspector, skipping through the pages, which were mostly filled with descriptions of black masses, witches' covens and magic sex orgies. A heavy man, broad-shouldered and thick in the middle, he had a blond close-cropped head which appeared to be connected to his body without benefit of neck. 'Girl, I should say, and young. Probably under twenty. Some of this may be imagination.'

'If it really is a young girl, I would hope that all of it is,' said the sergeant gravely. He was a handsome, unsmiling man with regular features and a near military bearing. He did not look in the least like a detective.

'Doesn't make any difference as far as we're concerned,' said the inspector. 'The question is, "Has it anything to do with this chap's death?" and I don't think it has. This was some kid he was making it with and she left her diary here. Probably so high on something or other she didn't know she had a diary or a place to leave it.'

'She could have been the reason he committed

suicide,' said the sergeant. 'I've seen this sort of thing before. These guest workers get in bed with some of the local talent who are out for sex and kicks or just trying to be "in" and they think it's true love. When they find out it's nothing, they crack up and kill themselves or somebody else.'

'Could be,' said the inspector. 'Well, all we can do is wait until Reichenauer tells us whether it was suicide or not. We'll see then.'

Reichenauer was Dr Otto Reichenauer, the greying, sad-faced medical expert attached to the criminal investigations department of the Duesseldorf police, who was now examining the body sitting on the sofa. He was not the only medical expert for the police, but he was the one who happened to be on duty at the time the report was received.

That had been at a little after six in the afternoon of Monday, 31 May 1982, a pleasant, sunny, late spring day in Duesseldorf, a city of close to three-quarters of a million inhabitants on the Rhine to the south of Bonn.

The person making the report was another guest worker, as the Germans call the cheap labour imported to keep down local wage levels, a thirty-year-old Spaniard named Manuel Hernandez.

Hernandez had said that he was a friend of the dead man, twenty-nine-year-old Jose Luis Mato Fernandez. Both came from Orense, a village not far from the Portuguese border, and both were employed on the same construction project in Duesseldorf.

Fernandez, known as Mato, had not turned up for work that Monday and Manuel went to his friend's apartment at 6 Metzger Strasse in the Derendorf area after he finished work to see what was wrong. The German economy was in a depression and an unexcused absence could easily cost a guest worker his job.

Mato did not need a job, however. He was sitting on the sofa in his living room, completely naked except for a shirt, which was open down the front. The handle of what looked to Manuel like a very large butcher's knife was sticking rigidly from his chest. Mato's right hand was resting on the handle of the knife and it was covered with blood. So too was the rest of Mato and most of the sofa.

The blood was not red, but dull brown and dry, so it was obvious that he had been stabbed some considerable time earlier.

Manuel, who had had experience in butchering pigs and other animals, did not doubt that his friend was dead and he did not approach the corpse, but quietly closed the door and went away to the Derendorf police sub-station.

The desk sergeant in the charge room had kept him there and sent a patrol car to investigate. When the report was confirmed, he alerted the department of criminal investigations at headquarters and the inspector, the sergeant and the doctor had come out.

The doctor concluded his on-the-spot examination and voiced the opinion that it was suicide. After all, the man's hand was still resting on the handle of the knife and the location of the wound was where it would be if he had wanted to stab himself through the heart.

Death had taken place some time early that morning, said the doctor, probably before ten o'clock. He would provide a more exact time in his report when he had completed the autopsy. The immediate cause of death was massive blood loss and he thought that the knife had probably gone through the heart itself.

'Okay,' said the inspector. 'You stay here, Peter, and I'll send out a team from the lab to go through all this stuff. There has to be an inventory for the final report and for the next of kin, if there is any. Probably be a question of who pays for the burial.'

Guest workers all had huge families while they were alive, but dead ones were often found to have no relatives at all.

The sergeant nodded and went out to the patrol car

to smoke a cigarette while he waited. The atmosphere within the apartment was not to his liking. The place was filthy and the kitchenette floor had apparently been used as a garbage bucket. There were old rags and junk lying all over and it smelled as if thirty or forty people had been holding a non-stop sex orgy for the past year or so.

The inspector and the doctor went back to headquarters and, after an hour's wait, the technicians turned up. There is enough crime in Duesseldorf for the laboratory to be manned round the clock, but they had had other matters to attend to.

And less disgusting, as they complained to the sergeant. Making an inventory of a place like that was more like cleaning cesspools than police work.

The sergeant pointed out that, if they did not like the work, they were free to seek employment elsewhere and suggested they got on with it. He did not like being there any more than they did and he could not leave until they had finished.

Thus encouraged, the technicians set to with a will and, by nine o'clock, the sergeant was able to report in to the inspector that operations at the scene had been terminated.

The corpse and the rooms of the apartment had been photographed as found. A scale diagram of the premises had been prepared. Everything that was not actual dirt or garbage had been sealed in plastic sacks and taken to the laboratory and the corpse had been transferred to the morgue. A neat, efficient job, carried out precisely according to the regulations, which was the way the sergeant did everything.

Having come on duty at two in the afternoon, the inspector and the sergeant went off duty at ten. The doctor, who kept different hours, had gone home immediately after completing his examination of the corpse.

He came in the following day at eight and began the

autopsy almost at once so that, by the time the inspector turned up in his office at two-thirty, he was nearly finished.

The sergeant, as was fitting, had arrived earlier than his chief and was engaged in going through the diary which had been found in the apartment the evening before.

'Hot stuff, eh, Peter?' said the inspector, lowering his two hundred plus pounds cautiously into his desk chair. 'Any indication of the identity of the author?'

The sergeant radiated unvoiced disapproval of the choice of language.

'Only that it was a girl,' he said. 'What she claims to have done at these devil-worshipping ceremonies wouldn't be physically possible for a man. We could probably trace her. She describes herself as the official high priestess of the Flingern devil-worshipping society.'

'If she's so popular in Flingern, what was she doing in Derendorf?' said the inspector, who did not regard the matter seriously.

Flingern was on the eastern edge of the city and Derendorf was to the north.

'Sleeping with guest workers,' said the sergeant matter-of-factly. 'She mentions this one by name.'

He turned the pages, cleared his throat and read: ' "*Lucifer, Lord of Darkness. Give me a sign. I believe in Thee. I want to belong to Thee. Come to me when Mato sleeps.*" '

'Any mention if he turned up?' said the inspector.

The sergeant closed the diary and put it in the drawer of the desk. 'I'll go and see whether Reichenauer is finished with the autopsy,' he said.

The doctor had not finished completely, but he had opened up the body and removed the knife from Fernandez's chest. It was an ordinary butcher's knife with a worn, much used blade some nine inches long.

'Terrible cut,' said the doctor. 'There's a hole here you can put your hand through. The third rib is completely

37

severed and the second part way. Went into the right chamber of the heart.'

'Hesitation cuts?' said the sergeant.

It was rare that the corpse of a suicide did not show shallow, tentative 'hesitation cuts' made while working up to the final act.

The doctor shook his head. 'This was a stab wound,' he said. 'It's more when they cut their wrists that you get hesitation cuts. Of course, he may have pricked himself on the chest a couple of times before he rammed it in, but those marks would be obliterated by the cut. On the other hand . . .'

'On the other hand what?' said the sergeant.

'I've never seen a man stab himself with such force before,' said the doctor. 'He must have been half out of his mind.'

'But it was him and not somebody else?' said the sergeant. 'You're certain?'

'Oh, I don't think there's much doubt of that,' said the doctor. 'I sent the knife over to Weapons Identification and they say it's his fingerprints on it.'

The sergeant inquired as to the time of death and was informed that it was at around nine on the morning of Monday. He then returned to his own office.

'Reichenauer thinks there's something funny with the case,' he said. 'He doesn't want to say so because he's already declared it suicide, but he's got doubts. I know him.'

'Well, if it wasn't suicide, then it was murder,' said the inspector. 'It sure as hell wasn't any accident. What else did Reichenauer say?'

'That the victim's last moments were happy,' said the sergeant. 'He was engaged in sex such a short time prior to his death that he hadn't washed yet.'

The inspector snorted. 'Reichenauer thinks there's something funny? I think there's something funny with Reichenauer. What kind of a suicide is this supposed to be anyway? A construction worker from some whistle-stop in Spain gets it off with one of our young idealists and his sensitive nature is so wounded by something she said or did that he rams a knife into himself with enough force to butcher an ox – and that at nine in the morning of a Monday? If that was all it took, we wouldn't have a guest worker alive in Germany.'

'Maybe it was his first experience with one of our local girls,' said the sergeant. 'I take it you want to open an investigation?'

The inspector did, and one of the first things which the sergeant found out was that whoever Jose Luis Mato Fernandez had spent his last night on earth with, it had definitely not been his first experience with the local girls.

Fernandez was, in fact, mildly famous in certain circles and proudly bore the nickname of Five-a-Night, which referred to his ability to perform intercourse five times a night on a more or less regular basis.

The sergeant had no difficulty in locating great numbers of witnesses to this feat, all of whom claimed personal experience, and some of whom were of an age that would have got Fernandez a jail sentence had he been alive to serve it.

None of the ladies was, however, able to provide any suggestion as to who might have wanted to murder the gallant Spaniard. Indeed, many expressed the opinion that such a person would be out of his or her mind. Certainly, no woman would have done it.

'They're probably right,' said the sergeant, reporting to the inspector on his progress. 'I don't think any woman could have done it unless she was a weightlifter or something. Nine inches of blade straight through two ribs? That takes force.'

'What does Reichenauer say?' asked the inspector. 'Does he think a woman would have had the strength?'

'He says it's not pertinent,' said the sergeant. 'He's sticking to his original theory of suicide.'

The doctor was having more and more difficulty in

defending his theory now the investigation had begun; Fernandez was proving to be not a very likely candidate for suicide.

His life had been largely an open book and his friend Manuel Hernandez was able to tell the police almost anything they wanted to know about him.

He was not a complex character. An unskilled construction worker from a small, provincial town, he had come, like so many others, to Germany seeking the work and relatively high wages that were not to be had in Spain.

He had been in the country a little over eight years at the time of his death and had never been in any kind of trouble. Hernandez and his other friends described him as normal in every respect, a hard, conscientious worker who liked a glass or two in the café after work, but not a heavy drinker. He had an easy-going nature, had not got into fights and had many friends.

The only thing exceptional about him was that he had a reputation for unusual sexual staying-power. This had attracted numbers of young German girls who were, as they described it, gathering experience. Perhaps for this reason, Fernandez had not married.

Finally, there was one other aspect to the character of Mato Fernandez and it was one which the inspector did not like. A man of high principles, he had never knowingly become involved with married women or women who were formally engaged.

This was a set-back to the investigation. The inspector's theory of the murder – as it was now formally classified – was that Fernandez had met his end at the hands of an outraged husband or fiancé.

'Could also have been a father or a brother,' suggested the sergeant helpfully. 'Or, maybe, she was married and he didn't know it.'

The inspector did not think so. Practically all of the girls with whom Fernandez was known to have been intimate were so promiscuous that outraged fathers or brothers would have had to take up murdering full-time. And as for the lady being married without Fernandez' knowledge, why were there no married women among the legion that the sergeant had contacted?

'No,' said the inspector. 'It's something else. We're barking up the wrong tree or, maybe, Reichenauer is right after all.'

'I don't think so,' said the sergeant. 'The more I think about that knife wound, the less likely it seems to me that it would have been self-inflicted. I just can't imagine a man like Fernandez slamming a knife into his own chest with such force. If he had been some kind of a psycho, yes, but from everything we've learned about him, he was completely normal, apart from being a little over-sexed. I think we should try to trace the girl who left that diary in his apartment.'

'It wasn't any of his playmates you've talked to so far?' said the inspector.

The sergeant shook his head. 'None of them admitted to being devil-worshippers and the girl in the diary was into devil-worshipping in a big way. People like that are nuts to begin with. She could have killed him for some weird reason, like, say, the devil wanted it.'

'You may be reading too much cheap literature,' said the inspector, 'but go ahead. See if you can locate her. We don't have a great deal else to try anyway.'

It was true. Nearly all the possibilities in the investigation had been exhausted. There were no suspects and there was no indication of any motive for the murder of Mato Fernandez. He had had an active sex life and he had lived, off and on, with an almost endless series of enthusiastic German girls, but there was no reason in the world for any of them to want to kill him. A great many of his compatriots lived in a like manner, even if they were not capable of five performances a night.

The sergeant, although he had not mentioned it, had another reason for wanting to trace the owner of the diary. He suspected that she had been Fernandez' companion at the time of his death.

This could mean that she had lived at the apartment, possibly for lack of any other place to live, which, in turn, would have made her, in Mato's eyes, a dependent female and in need of supervision. For Mato, whose standards were those of his native village, had believed strongly that it was the duty of the male to enforce morality in the weaker sex.

This was obviously not a point of view which would have found much acceptance among the totally liberated, near insanely independent German teens with whom the Spaniard had shared his reeking bed.

The sergeant was wondering whether there might not have been a sort of cultural clash. A self-proclaimed queen of the devil-worshippers might not have been prepared to accept the authority of a Spanish peasant whose devotion to the double standard would have appeared outdated to her grandmother.

There was, of course, the trying question of why the young lady would have found it necessary to murder Fernandez. It would scarcely have been because she was emotionally involved. The sergeant knew what kind of a girl she was. Most such girls were emotionally burned out before they had passed their teens.

The motive would, therefore, be something weird, possibly incomprehensible to the ordinary person, and what more weird than devil-worship, black masses and witches' covens, all of which had featured prominently in the diary?

Although the owner of the diary was not identified by name, the entries were dated. The lady expressed a wish that Lucifer visit her while Mato was asleep on 30 April, exactly one month before Mato was stabbed.

Whether this had any significance, it did place her in Mato's apartment on that date. All that was necessary to identify her was to determine who Fernandez had been living with at the time.

42

This proved to be impossible. There had been heavy traffic in Mato's bedroom and it was not always clear who was resident and who was not. Probably Mato had not known himself. In any case, no one had had any particular reason to keep track and, after such a length of time, no one could remember.

Having encountered failure in this respect, the sergeant went back to the diary, wading through such unmaidenly appeals as, '*Lucifer, Lord of Darkness! I would sell my soul to Thee! I would help Thee bring ruin over the world. Give me a sign, Lord!*' and some remarkably graphic descriptions of sex orgies, involving persons who were apparently multi-sexual, until he found the reference to the Flingern devil-worshippers.

He had hoped that there would be details to aid him in his search, but all there were were boasts of how no coven or black mass in Flingern was complete without the body of the high priestess serving as an altar.

· The language left no doubt that the high priestess and the author of the diary were the same person.

It also left no doubt that, if there was anything sexual in the world which the high priestess and author had not personally experienced, it was because it was physically impossible or cost money.

The sergeant, therefore, took himself off to Flingern and began asking questions. As he was not known there and did not look like a police officer, he was soon able to learn that there was, indeed, an active and flourishing devil-worshipping society and was even able to obtain an application form for admission to it.

Devil-worshippers or not, the society remained German, and Germans liked things done in an orderly manner – which meant admission forms, membership cards, minutes of the meetings and, presumably, dues.

The sergeant did not sign up, partly because he would have been unable to justify the cost on his expense voucher and partly because he sincerely had no desire to belong to an organization for worshipping the devil.

Membership, moreover, was not necessary as the high priestess was publicity-conscious and her identity was easily learned.

High Priestess Sylvia Brakel was twenty-two years old, which was older than the sergeant had expected, but she did not look her age, having a pretty, round, baby face and a good deal of soft, long, blonde hair. Given a Girl Guide uniform and a book of raffle tickets to sell, she would not have looked out of character.

None the less, Sylvia was a genuine devil-worshipper, a witch, a past mistress in the art of the protracted sex orgy and the author of the diary found in Mato Fernandez' apartment.

The sergeant did not immediately take her into custody or even question her concerning her relationship to Fernandez, but began trying to identify her closer friends. He was able to turn up three of these, all nearly as weird as Sylvia herself.

The first and oldest was a twenty-four-year-old journeyman baker who rarely worked at his trade, but who was very active in devil-worshipping circles. His name was Christian Berger and he was proud to tell anyone who would listen that it was he who had introduced the high priestess to devil-worshipping before she had reached the age of eighteen.

Her other male confidant was twenty-nine-year-old Detlef Meister, a lorry driver. He did not drive lorries much more than Christian Berger baked bread. He too was a born-again devil-worshipper.

The third friend was technically female, but preferred not to think so. Nineteen-year-old Susi Boettcher had been a convinced lesbian from the time she was at school and referred to Sylvia as 'my wife'.

Having assembled this information on Sylvia Brakel and her friends, the sergeant presented it to the inspector and asked for instructions. There was no evidence against any of them, but Sylvia had been living with

Fernandez not long before he was murdered and he felt that they were all weird enough for anything.

So did the inspector, and he promptly ordered the sergeant to take all four into custody and grill them as hard as he dared. He was not very confident of the outcome. It was rare that an admission of anything could be extracted from such hard-bitten types.

Both the inspector and the sergeant had overlooked one thing, however. All of the suspects were devil-worshippers.

And devil-worshippers, of course, have reverse morals. You do not stick with your friends. You betray them.

Taken into custody, Christian Berger, Detlef Meister and Susi Boettcher all immediately denounced Sylvia Brakel as the murderess of Mato Fernandez. She had, they said, told them so herself.

Indeed, she had – and she was quite prepared to tell Sergeant Froebes too. She did not seem in the least concerned that this would lead to her being tried for murder. She did not seem concerned about anything.

Sylvia said she had murdered Mato because he objected to her sleeping with other men and women and taking part in sex orgies while she was living with him. It reflected, he had said, on his honour.

They had quarrelled over this previously, but Sunday night, 30 May was the final straw.

She came home at five in the morning after an exhausting black mass in which she had served not only as high priestess and altar, but also as object of the membership's most far-out fantasies, to find Mato waiting up for her.

There was another quarrel and she came to the conclusion that the best solution would be to kill him.

She waited until he fell asleep on the sofa, fetched the knife from the kitchen and, using both hands, drove it into his chest with a swing.

She aimed for the heart, she said, and added proudly that Mato never knew what hit him.

She then put his hand on the handle of the knife so that the police would think it was suicide, and went off to be comforted by Susi.

Sylvia's trial was very well attended and the audience was not disappointed.

She described how she and her grandfather had practised mutual masturbation when she was eight, how she had been gang-banged by a group of rockers when she was sixteen and how she had become the high priestess of the devil-worshippers through sheer sex power. She had, she admitted, a more than casual interest in sex, which was why she had been living with the famous Five-a-Night.

Sylvia expressed the opinion that her character had been warped by being sent to reform school for shoplifting while yet a child, but the court was not impressed. As she had been found, rather surprisingly, sane and competent to stand trial, they sentenced her to life imprisonment on 25 March 1983.

She greeted the verdict with the same indifference she had displayed toward everything else.

4

FIT TO BE TIED

As a general rule, whores tend to sympathize with other whores.

Although nominally competitors, they are all in much the same boat and it is not always the luxury liner that the uninitiated believe it to be.

The work is tiring and often unpleasant. Handsome, sexually normal young men do not need to frequent prostitutes. The service is available elsewhere free. The prostitute can be happy, therefore, if her clients are clean, young enough to get it over with quickly and not practising sadists.

Calculated on the basis of an hourly rate, the younger, more attractive practitioners are well-paid, but there is often little left of these high gross earnings. Maintaining a serious, conscientious pimp is expensive, and not many are prepared to run the risk of doing without one. For prostitution, as any insurance agent will tell you, is a dangerous profession. In terms of personal security, it is wiser to become a trapeze artist.

Karin Lewandowski had not had a pimp and so she was, of course, dead, her throat cut from ear to ear.

She had been a pretty woman, dark-haired, admirably curved, and she had not looked much more than half of her forty-one years.

Even so, business had been a little slack in recent years and one reason that Karin had not had a pimp was because she was too old to attract an acceptable one. It did not take a very bright pimp to estimate the number of years of top earning power left in that forty-year-old body, and why bother when the woods were full of enthusiastic eighteen-year-olds?

Karin had, therefore, run her business single-handed from apartment 846 of the towering Pharao House in the Oberfoehring sector of Munich. Had her throat not been cut, she might have been able to put aside a little something for her retirement from the savings on pimp fees.

As it was, although not retired in the conventional sense, she had definitely gone out of business – and she came close to taking her last customer with her.

He was a good customer, too, a regular who had a fixed appointment for every second Sunday at four-thirty in the afternoon.

However, the gentleman, who will here be known as Karl-Otto Schmidt, was slightly overweight and over-age, and when he pushed open the door of Karin's studio apartment to find her lying on the bed, bound, gagged and soaked in blood, he very nearly had a heart attack.

This would have been embarrassing as Karl-Otto was a respectable businessman and married. Unfortunately, his wife was not fond of sex or, at least, not with Karl-Otto. As a result, although he was spared the heart attack, he did end up with a bad headache from trying to decide what he should do.

Karin was dead, obviously murdered, and the logical thing to do was to telephone the police.

If he did that, however, he might be arrested, interrogated, required to appear as a witness and end up on the front pages of the newspapers. He could already see before his eyes a vision of his wife squinting in disbelief at his picture and the caption 'Local Businessman Discovers Dead Whore', or something similar.

Well then, simply close the door and steal quietly away. Let someone else report the murder. After all, there was no hurry. Karin was not going anywhere.

But had she left something behind? A list of customers? He knew that she kept an appointment book.

She was rather forgetful. And his name was in it, he was certain. After all, he had been visiting her for over two years now. What would happen when the police traced the four-thirty appointment and found it was him? How could he explain having failed to report the crime?

He would be lucky if he was not charged with the murder himself.

Gritting his teeth and trying to calculate how much in the way of a property settlement his wife might get in the event of a divorce, he picked up Karin Lewandowski's telephone and dialled the emergency number of the police.

He was, he said, at the scene of a murder. Yes, he would wait for the police to arrive.

The officer in the communications centre at the huge police headquarters building kept him on the telephone for an unconscionable length of time, spelling out the address, confusing his name three or four times and giving him the impression that he was speaking to a mentally deficient police officer.

The point of all this was, of course, to keep Karl-Otto on the telephone until a patrol car could arrive and determine whether he was a madman, a drug addict on a bad trip, an alcoholic, a practical joker or whether there really had been a murder.

Following confirmation by the patrol car officers, the duty homicide squad was called away. This consisted of a remarkably bland-looking detective inspector named Ralf Dormann, a huge-limbed, red-haired and freckled sergeant of detectives named Sepp Heide and a medical expert named Leopold Langenauer, who habitually bore the slightly troubled look of a bank clerk who is wondering whether his accounts are really in order.

The inspector, a basically compassionate man, examined Karl-Otto's personal identification papers, listened to his explanation of how he came to discover the body and then assured him that his real name would never be revealed by the police and, as a matter of fact, it never was.

In the meantime, Sergeant Heide had been going through the small kitchen and bathroom to see if there were any indications of robbery. Prostitutes were generally killed by persons who mistakenly believed that they kept large sums of cash on the premises.

Although the sergeant did find signs of a search – and, apparently, a successful one, for there was not a cent in the apartment – Dr Langenauer did not favour robbery as a motive.

The victim, he pointed out, had been bound, gagged and, he thought, chloroformed. There was still a strong smell of chloroform around the bed.

She had obviously been entertaining a client, for she was wearing nothing other than black net stockings, a black suspender belt and a white blouse.

The blouse was now largely red, and so was the bed, the wall and part of the ceiling. Beneath the woman's chin gaped an enormous wound stretching across the neck from side to side. It had been made, said the doctor, with a straight razor or something equally sharp.

Karin's hands were bound behind her back and the end of the cord had been brought up and fastened around her neck in a slip noose. The bonds were drawn very tight and had cut into the skin.

Her feet were not bound and her legs were sprawled wide as if she had been making a deliberate effort to get them as far apart as possible.

Proceeding to the examination of the genitals, the doctor found out why.

'There's a double-edged razor blade inside the vagina,' he said. 'She didn't dare to move for fear of cutting herself.'

'Pervert then?' said the inspector.

'Definitely,' said the doctor. 'Bondage, sadism, what-have-you. There should be something on this boy in the files. It's unlikely that this is his first offence.'

50

'We'll see,' said the inspector. 'What do you find, Sepp?'

'Not much,' said the sergeant. 'I think he went through the place and took whatever money he could find. Nothing else obvious missing. I don't suppose she would have kept any real jewellery here in the shop.'

'Have to see whether she had a private residence,' said the inspector. 'Well, let's get the lab people out here and see what they turn up. When can I have the autopsy report, Leo?'

'Before noon tomorrow,' said the doctor. 'By the way, she's only been dead a couple of hours.'

'You'd better call out a detail to canvass the building and see if anybody noticed anything, Sepp,' said the inspector. 'Let me know what you turn up. I'll be in the office.'

The laboratory technicians did not find anything of apparent significance in Karin Lewandowski's apartment. There had been a great many persons there, presumably men, which was what might be expected in the business premises of a practising prostitute, but there was nothing to connect any of them to the murder. They agreed with the sergeant that the place had been searched for money, but there was no certainty as to whether any had been found.

After they had finished and the body had been photographed, it was taken to the police morgue to await the autopsy the following morning.

The technicians went home, but Sergeant Heide and his men remained until nearly midnight, questioning the tenants of the building and interfering seriously with business, as most of them were engaged in the same activity as Karin had been. They were not told at this time that she had been murdered.

The murder, but few details of the circumstances, was announced in the newspapers the following morning. Solidarity among prostitutes is never stronger than when one of them is murdered, so a number of telephone calls were received at police headquarters from colleagues who had known Karin or who had recently had particularly weird clients.

Most of these were of no value to the investigation, but two were of possible significance.

Thirty-year-old Anna Brucker reported that she had had a client who wanted her to get into a white blouse and allow him to tie her up. She had refused to be tied as she was afraid of being left helpless, but she had put on a white blouse. The man had not been able to achieve orgasm and had become threatening. She had responded by taking the leash off her Dobermann and he had left. She described him as young, in his middle twenties, good-looking, less than average height, clean, well-groomed and well-dressed.

The other potential lead was from thirty-two-year-old Marta Siebrach who reported a similar, but more alarming experience. She had, unwisely, allowed the man to tie her and had been frightened nearly out of her wits when he inserted a double-edged razor blade into her vagina. He had said that it was so that she would hold still. He had also pulled the bonds much too tight before achieving his orgasm. Afterwards, he had been apologetic, had removed the razor blade and had untied her. He had given her some extra money, but she would have gladly renounced payment to get him out of the apartment. She thought he was crazy.

Marta Siebrach had also been asked to put on a white blouse, and this led the inspector to believe it was the same man as Anna Brucker's client and, possibly, the murderer of Karin Lewandowski.

Unfortunately, Anna and Marta could only provide descriptions. Neither had had any indication of the customer's identity and, although both spent the best part of a day going through the police mug books, they were unable to find any picture resembling the man in question.

Nothing useful had turned up in the autopsy report

either. Karin had died at approximately two o'clock in the afternoon and she had been unconscious from chloroform at the time. The murderer had made two slight cuts in her neck with the razor, before taking the full sweep which had opened her throat to the backbone. He had apparently failed to achieve orgasm as there was no semen in or on the body.

By this time, everyone known to have been in or near the Pharao House on Sunday had been contacted and interrogated and had their stories checked. There were no suspects.

There were also no witnesses who reported seeing anyone suspicious-looking in the building, but this was not significant. If the killer was the same man who had frightened Anna Brucker and Marta Slebrach, he did not look suspicious.

The identification section had collected a few hundred latent fingerprints from the apartment and some of them were of persons with police records. None had records of attacks on women, however, and, in any case, none of the fingerprints were so placed as to show a direct connection with the crime.

Karin's appointment book, which had so troubled Karl-Otto Schmidt, had been found, but it proved valueless. The only entries were those of first names, nicknames and terse descriptions, not all of them flattering. Karin had apparently been considerate in not wanting to compromise her customers in the event the book fell into the wrong hands.

The inspector was not too dismayed by this circumspection. He had not expected much from the appointment book anyway, as he assumed that it contained only the names of Karin's regular customers. The murderer had not been a regular.

Who he could have been was just about any male in Munich. Karin had not exactly had a walk-in business, but she had run permanent advertisements in the classified sections of two newspapers which, although they varied a little in text, left no doubt with the reader that the friendly services for reasonable fees that she was offering involved a degree of physical contact. She did not give the address, only the telephone number, and recommended that interested parties ring for an appointment.

'A little like Russian roulette,' remarked the sergeant. 'She never knew what she was going to get.'

'Neither do we,' said the inspector. 'And we're not as well-paid. Well, let's release a little more information to the press and see if that brings in anything. They should be happy to cooperate. After all, she was an advertiser.'

The little more information which the inspector had in mind was details of the kinky aspects of the case and, particularly, the white blouse, which was thought to have been furnished by the murderer as it was not Karin's size.

This could be significant, for in the case of Marta Siebrach, the client had provided a white blouse when she had said that she had none. Anna Brucker had had a white blouse, so it was not known whether her caller had brought one with him or not.

A rather lurid account of the circumstances of Karin's death appeared in the newspapers the following day and, the day after that, there was a response.

A forty-year-old woman named Helga Braun telephoned police headquarters to say she thought she might have some information concerning the Karin Lewandowski murder and who should she tell it to?

The switchboard officer said someone would come to take her statement and, in about five minutes, Sergeant Heide was there.

The haste was justified, for what Mrs Braun had was the first promising lead in the case.

Mrs Braun, who described herself as divorced, without friends and lonely, said that something had gone wrong with her telephone on 10 February and she had consequently called the repair service and asked for an engineer.

One had been sent round, an attractive young man in his mid-twenties, very neat, almost handsome, although a little smaller than average.

The young man had fixed her telephone and accepted a cup of coffee after he had finished. Just how it had happened she could not say, but the conversation had come around to sex and the young man, who never once mentioned his name, confessed that he had certain problems in achieving sexual satisfaction.

Mrs Braun had inquired as to what they might be and, after some embarrassed hemming and hawing around, he had replied that he was able to achieve orgasm only if his partner was wearing a white blouse and allowed him to tie her up.

The lonely divorcee had said that she had a white blouse and that she had no objections to being tied up as long as it was not too tight.

She had then removed her clothing and put on the white blouse. The man had also removed his clothing and tied her up with her bathrobe cord. They had engaged in intercourse and he had subsequently declared himself fully satisfied with the results.

So too was Mrs Braun, but, later on, she had begun to wonder whether she had not done something foolish. The man was a total stranger and while she was tied, she had been completely at his mercy. Pleasant as the encounter had been, it was not, she decided, something that she would risk again. Later, she had read the account of the Lewandowski murder in the newspaper and been so stuck by the similarity with her own experience that she decided to contact the police.

The police were duly grateful. Although the young man had not identified himself to Mrs Braun, his identity could easily be traced. Telephone service in Germany is provided by the postal service, and there would be an exact record of who had been sent to repair Mrs Braun's telephone.

Having taken Mrs Braun's statement and refused a cup of coffee, the sergeant went straight to the telephone service section of the post office.

When he returned to police headquarters, it was with the name and address of a man who liked to tie women up while they were wearing a white blouse and nothing else.

This telephone engineer was named Wolfgang Siegfried Grabatsch. He was twenty-five years old. He came from a good, middle-class family. He had never been in any kind of trouble. And he lived in the nearby village of Erding with his lovely nineteen-year-old wife, Brigitte.

To any ordinary person, Grabatsch would have appeared the most unlikely suspect in the world, but the officers of the homicide squad were well aware that criminals, even seriously disturbed psychopaths, do not have an appearance differing from the most law-abiding of citizens.

Juries are not, however, composed of police officers and appearance does count in the courtroom. If Grabatsch was the murderer of Karin Lewandowski, then the police were going to have to present solid evidence if they hoped to obtain an indictment, let alone a conviction.

The inspector knew, however, that there was no evidence to be obtained from the scene and that there would probably be no witnesses. If there was any proof at all, it would have to be obtained from Grabatsch himself.

He, therefore, approached the matter as carefully as if he were walking on soap bubbles. It was of utter importance that Grabatsch not be alarmed into destroying or disposing of any evidence there might be.

The first step was to find out just how good a suspect Grabatsch was.

He was, without question, the telephone engineer who

had taken care of Helga Braun's telephone and other problems, but he had not harmed her in any way. Bondage was a common enough perversion and, although the white blouse was unusual, clothing fetishes were not.

With Anna Brucker and, particularly, Marta Siebrach, the matter had been less harmless and more like the murder of Karin Lewandowski. The question was: Was this the same man?

There was only one way to find out and the inspector, with some assistance from telephone service supervisors, arranged for Anna Brucker and Marta Siebrach to obtain a look at Grabatsch without his knowledge.

Both immediately identified him as the man with a taste for bondage and white blouses.

This, the inspector felt, was enough or, rather, all he was going to get, and he immediately took Grabatsch into custody, brought his wife to police headquarters for questioning and searched his house and car very thoroughly.

The search did not need to be so thorough. Everything the police found was easily located for no effort had been made to conceal it.

In the trunk of the car was a tidy kit containing a bottle of chloroform, gauze compresses for applying it to the nose and mouth, adhesive tape, rubber gloves, a pair of tights and two white blouses.

In the house was one of the most impressive collections of pornography that the arresting officers had ever seen. It was heavily concentrated on bondage and included books, magazines, video tapes, films and photographs. Many of the photographs had been taken by Grabatsch himself for the subject was his wife, trussed like a turkey, wearing a white blouse and smiling into the camera. An obvious believer in the do-it-yourself principle, he had also composed a number of the typewritten pornographic manuscripts, featuring, of course, women tied up while wearing white blouses.

Significantly, there was no straight razor or any other weapon and, for a time, the inspector feared that his suspect was going to slip through his fingers.

The material found in Grabatsch's house was proof that he was profoundly interested in pornography and bondage, but so were a few thousand others in Munich.

The equipment in the trunk of the car was more incriminating for it included items such as had been used in the Lewandowski murder. There was, however, no proof that these items had been used in the murder or that it was Grabatsch who had used them.

If Grabatsch denied the crime and stuck to his story, there was little hope of indicting him and none at all of obtaining a conviction.

But Grabatsch did not deny the murder and, in fact, expressed relief that he had been apprehended. Had he not been, he said, there was no telling how many women he might have killed. He was, he added with rare under-statement, a man with serious mental problems.

Wolfgang Siegfried Grabatsch was not only an amateur author of bondage pornography, but an amateur psychol-ogist as well. He was able to present the police with a thorough analysis of the personality problems which had caused him to become a murderer.

It had all started, he said, when he was only six years old. His grandmother, who was seventy at the time, had been taken to hospital. When he asked what was the matter with her, his mother regaled him with a remark-able story to tell a child of his age.

His seventy-four-year-old grandfather, she said, had insisted that Grandma dress up in an abbreviated costume of no more than a pair of high heels and black net stockings and had chased her through the house until she jumped out of a window in terror and broke her leg.

This event had made a profound impression on Wolfgang.

A few months later, he was playing indians with his eight-year-old cousin, Lilian Boos. Lilian persuaded him to take off his clothes, tied him up and took liberties with his private parts. At the time, she was wearing only a white blouse.

This had made an even stronger impression on him and he was never able to enjoy normal sexual relations, although he made several attempts.

Finally, in 1976, when he was twenty, he met a girl named Angelika Faber, two years his junior but not entirely inexperienced in sexual matters. He felt at ease with Angelika and managed to confess his secret fantasy of tying up a girl in a white blouse and making love to her.

Like Mrs Braun, Angelika had a white blouse and no objections to being tied up. They spent many happy hours, but there was an unfortunate tendency to tie the bonds tighter and tighter and Angelika eventually decided that she did not want to play that game any more. At the beginning of 1977, she dissolved their romance.

However, Wolfgang now knew what he wanted and how to get it. Making the acquaintance of Brigitte, who was only fifteen at the time, he had her bound, bloused and pregnant in a little over six weeks.

Far from being dismayed at the prospect of father-hood, Grabatsch proposed to marry the girl, but, as this was violently opposed by her family and as she was still under the legal age, the marriage did not take place and Brigitte had an abortion instead.

Embittered, Wolfgang returned to Angelika, but, again, the bonds were too tight for her liking and on 12 September 1980, he and Brigitte were married. A remarkably understanding woman, she permitted him to keep the large collection of pornographic pictures which he had made of her predecessor.

Nor did she fail him now. Her husband might be a murderer and a sex psychopath, but, as far as she was concerned, he was a good husband and she was prepared to wait until he had served his sentence, whatever that might be.

It could have been a long wait, although no one really serves a life sentence in Germany today, but Wolfgang did not go to prison after all.

Having kept him under observation for some considerable time, the state psychologists agreed with his analysis that he had serious mental problems and recommended that he be sent not to prison, but to a psychiatric hospital where he would be recycled, reprogrammed and returned to the faithfully waiting Brigitte.

This is a common process and one that rarely takes very long.

Prostitution remains a dangerous profession.

In Munich, at least.

5

THE MURDER IS THE MOTIVE

During the summers of 1980, 1981 and 1982, someone was killing back-packers in France.

There was nothing very unusual about it. Someone was always killing back-packers in France and elsewhere. In the closing years of the twentieth century, all kinds of people were getting killed everywhere, so why not back-packers?

Formerly, it was hitch-hikers. Hitch-hikers were being decimated. And not surprisingly. If large numbers of nubile maidens chose to stand at roadsides and climb light-heartedly into the cars of total strangers, a certain percentage was going to get more than a free ride.

By the eighties, however, hitch-hikers were out and back-packers were in. Nobody was going to give a hitch-hiker a lift because they looked too much like hippies and everybody knew that hippies were all on drugs and would steal your car and murder you. Even girl hippies couldn't get lifts. Rapists too worry about venereal disease.

Back-packers were better, more sporting and wholesome. The idea was, the back-packer strode stoutly along, tent and gear strapped to his or her back, and with sturdy, but not necessarily unattractive legs roamed the Continent, healthily, ecologically and at modest cost.

In practice, the back-packer hitch-hiked. And, if the back-packer was female and pretty, she not infrequently got raped, killed, both or worse.

Contrary to popular belief, terminology does not change the world.

So what was so remarkable about those back-packers who died violent deaths in the first three years of the eighties?

To begin with, they were all men, young men, not particularly handsome, not particularly well-to-do and not homosexual.

But who, in heaven's name, would want to kill nonentities like these and for what reason?

Precisely.

Second, they were all killed by one or more bullets fired into their heads at point-blank range from a 7.65 mm pistol.

Third, they were all killed during the month of August.

And, finally, they were all asleep in their sleeping-bags at the time.

In short, the murderer killed young men quite deliberately while they were asleep and for neither sex nor money. No comprehensible motive. No prior contact between murderer and victim. No clues. And, apparently, no witnesses.

The French authorities could scarcely be blamed for failing to solve such crimes and, as a matter of fact, they were not.

Indeed, no one realized that there was a series of such crimes going on. The victims were not rich enough to attract sympathy and the scenes were scattered across France. Had there been more sex to the killings, even homosexual sex, the media might have shown greater interest, but who wanted to read about some young stranger getting himself shot while alone in a sleeping-bag?

Nobody, and so it is possible that the series actually began before 1980. There were a lot of points in the case that were never completely clear and the exact number of victims was one of them.

The first known victim was in Nice, the heart of the French Riviera and a place which attracts many persons in August, some of whom are back-packers.

This particular one was French. A twenty-two-year-old office employee named Claude Sevigny, he lived and worked in Paris. August was his vacation month, as it is for so many of the French.

The French economy being a near-permanent basket-case, Claude was grateful for having a job at all so he did not feel too badly about being underpaid. After all, he was young and unmarried. If he could not afford train fares and hotels on his holiday, he could back-pack and camp.

So he did. And came to Nice. During the night of Tuesday, 5 August 1980, at approximately eleven-forty-five, someone held the muzzle of a 7.65 mm pistol less than six inches from his head and pulled the trigger.

Claude died instantly and without waking up. Whatever hopes, ambitions or future he had had died with him. Sadly, the subsequent police investigation gave reason to believe that he had never even had a girl friend.

Nor many friends of any kind. His life had been uneventful. He was neither gifted nor stupid. He was neither rich nor terribly poor. He had passed his secondary school examination, but without distinction. He was not ugly, but he would never make it in the movies either. Like many young Frenchmen, he was somewhat shy.

Claude Sevigny was simply one of the ten or fifteen million members of his age group, a completely average young Frenchman.

So why would someone deliberately put a bullet through his head?

The sergeant of detectives assigned to finding out why had learned all these things about Claude Sevigny by the simple expedient of requesting a background report from the Paris police. They had responded promptly and thoroughly, but the answer had left the sergeant more

63

puzzled than before. There was no reason for anyone to kill Claude.

Except madness, a totally irrational act committed for the sake of the act itself and having nothing to do with the victim's identity.

As the sergeant pointed out in the report with which he closed the case, insanity was practically the only plausible motive. The victim had only been two days in Nice and knew no one in the area. He had had no romantic associations and very little money, less than a hundred francs, which was not enough to even eat regularly. Nor could the murderer have believed that he had money. People who spend nights in a cheap sleeping-bag laid out in a waste lot are rarely thought to be wealthy. But, even if the murderer was so stupid, why did he not take the money which he had killed to get?

The only answer, wrote the sergeant, was madness. The murder was the motive.

On the basis of past experience, it was feared that it would be repeated in the future. It had, of course, occurred to the sergeant that it might not have been the first, but a search of the records turned up no similar case in the area within the past ten years.

The sergeant, therefore, kept an eye out for new cases, and when none were reported along the Mediterranean coast, he came to the conclusion that the murderer had also been on holiday and had now gone home.

Unfortunately, the murder of Claude Sevigny aroused not much more interest with the police than with the media. The sergeant of detectives in Nice had developed a certain empathy for Claude through delving into his background, but he was practically the only police officer who knew that he had ever existed.

If he had looked along the Atlantic coast, he might have had more luck. On Thursday, 14 August, nine days after the murder of Claude Sevigny, twenty-year-old Bernard Marechal was shot to death in his sleeping-bag on a deserted beach near St Malo, an old pirate city on the coast of Brittany.

The sergeant in Nice would have recognized the circumstances immediately.

Bernard, who came from the city of Metz in the east of France, had been on holiday from his job as an apprentice plumber. He was asleep at the time he was shot through the head, twice this time, with a 7.65 mm pistol at close range. He had had almost no money and what he had was not taken. Unlike Claude Sevigny, he had had a girl friend, but she was only sixteen and their relationship had been chaste. Had she gone on holiday with him, it might have saved his life. Or cost her hers.

St Malo being a smaller place than Nice, it was an inspector from the department of criminal investigations who investigated the Marechal murder. Despite his superior rank, he was no more successful than the sergeant in Nice had been in solving his case, and eventually came to the same conclusion. The murder could only be the work of a madman. There was no motive.

The Bernard Marechal unsolved homicide joined the Claude Sevigny unsolved homicide in the memory of the central records section computer of the National Gendarmerie, and the computer no doubt recognized that the cases were similar, if not identical. However, no one asked it and so, computerlike, it held its peace.

It did not matter, in any case. There were no more clues in the Marechal case than there were in the Sevigny case.

If there were any more such killings during 1980, the reports of them did not find their way into the computer memory of the central records section.

There probably were none. Later, when efforts were made to determine the total number of victims, the computer was consulted and never came up with any numbers greater than those the police already knew. Two each for August 1980, 1981 and 1982.

That the murders fell only in this month was significant. It was the month when the murderer was on holiday and had time and opportunity for killing. The rest of the year, he was apparently too busy at his job.

As a lead, the knowledge was worthless. It merely indicated that the murderer was employed and that he took his holiday in August. This was true of around twenty million people in France.

People, because there was no proof that the murderer was a man and, as a matter of fact, the sergeant in Nice had considered the possibility of a female killer, possibly some maiden who had been wronged by a back-packer.

It was as good a theory as any, but it had a slightly comical sound to it and the sergeant did not mention it to his superiors.

What he did mention took place the following August and it was not a murder along the Mediterranean coast, but one in Normandy, which is even further to the north than St Malo. It was also not on the coast at all, but close to eighty miles inland near the town of Mondicourt.

The reason that the sergeant learned of it was that the victim came from Menton, which is just up the coast from Nice and on the border to Italy. The police in Mondicourt had requested background information in order to establish some sort of motive for the murder of twenty-four-year-old Jean-Pierre Lacosta, who had been killed on 12 August 1981 by two 7.65 mm bullets fired through his head at close range while he was asleep in his sleeping-bag. Lacosta had been unemployed and had had barely the money to buy a pack of cigarettes on him at the time.

The Mondicourt police had logically come to the conclusion that Jean-Pierre had been on more intimate terms with some lady than was conducive to his health, and this lady could only be in his home town as he had not been in Normandy long enough to render anyone jealous.

The sergeant found all this remarkably familiar and, having received a copy of the Menton police report

66

pointing to no known motive for the murder of Lacosta, he requested further details from Mondicourt concerning the circumstances of the case.

The circumstances were nearly identical to the Sevigny murder the year before and the sergeant immediately went to the commissioner who had had responsibility for the investigation of the case.

There was, he reported, evidence of what appeared to be a weird series. As it was taking place in widely separated regions of the country, he thought that it should be turned over to the department of criminal investigations of the National Gendarmerie.

The commissioner listened to the evidence and agreed.

Two days later, the Sevigny and Lacosta cases were formally turned over to Inspector Claude Descroix, a specialist in series murders, attached to the Homicide Division of the French National Gendarmerie.

Inspector Descroix and his assistant, Detective Sergeant Yves Saint, began their investigation by consulting the records and requesting information on any similar cases from police and gendarmerie units nationwide.

They immediately received the Marechal case from both the records section computer and the St Malo police.

They had barely had time to read through the file and note the nearly identical circumstances to the Sevigny and Lacosta murders when a fourth case was reported from the Atlantic coastal city of La Rochelle. An eighteen-year-old boy had been shot through the head while asleep in a sleeping-bag.

The inspector and the sergeant left immediately for La Rochelle. The murder had taken place on Sunday, 23 August 1981, and they had received notice of it on Monday morning. By Monday afternoon, they were at the scene.

This was the first opportunity that the gendarmerie investigators had had to observe the scene of one of the crimes committed by the Back-packer Murderer so soon after it had taken place. They were hoping for some indication that the La Rochelle police might have missed. Because of their specialized training and experience in the field, they were sometimes able to draw conclusions that local police investigators were not.

It was not to be the case here. Didier Vitry, who came from the city of Lyon on the opposite side of the country, had been a secondary school student. He had had almost no money. He had been back-packing and, on that Sunday evening, he had spread out his sleeping-bag and other equipment on a beach which, although near the city, was largely deserted because the pollution level of the water was too high to permit bathing. At approximately eleven o'clock, according to the autopsy report of the La Rochelle coroner, someone had held a 7.65 mm pistol within a few inches of his left temple and pulled the trigger. The bullet had gone straight through Vitry's head and exited on the right side, taking with it some fragments of bone and a fatal quantity of brain tissue. In so far as the investigators could determine, this was the closest that the murderer had come to the victim.

There was, however, one minor difference. Vitry's personal identification card was missing.

'Let's hope he didn't lose it,' said the inspector. 'If the killer took it, it's his first mistake and we may be able to make it his last.'

He was a short, plump, cheerful-looking man with rosy cheeks and twinkling blue eyes. With a white beard and white rather than brown hair, he could have passed for Santa Claus.

His assistant was a totally nondescript man with medium brown hair, medium brown eyes, medium build and the slightly concerned air of a not very successful insurance salesman.

'I'll get out a directive to all units to keep watch for it,' he said. 'He apparently moves around a good deal so one of the spot road checks might get him.'

The French police and gendarmerie make frequent road checks of vehicles. Mostly, they are looking for drugs or terrorists, but they could look for a stolen ID card as well.

The inspector and the sergeant returned to their base to wait for further reports. They were aware that the sergeant in Nice and some of the other investigators had come to the conclusion that the Back-packer Murderer killed only during August while he was on holiday, but this was no more than a theory and, in any case, August was not yet over.

It soon was, however, and the theory appeared to be correct for there were no more cases reported that year.

Nor the next year either, up until August. With the arrival of that fatal month, Inspector Descroix and Sergeant Saint began keeping an overnight bag packed. If there was any consistency in the murderer, he would soon strike again.

So far, it had been a frustrating case for the investigators. No trace of the missing ID card had turned up and there had been nothing else to investigate. All that they had been able to do with the case during the past eleven months had been to review what the local police had already done in the four murders in the hopes that something had been missed. Nothing had been.

It was a near certainty that, with the arrival of another August, yet more unsuspecting young men would be marked down for a pointless death and there was nothing that they could do about it. Warnings had, of course, been published in the newspapers and broadcast over the radio and television stations, but they had not noticeably reduced the number of back-packers on the roads.

'They're right, of course,' said the sergeant gloomily. 'The individual risk isn't high. Say there's fifty thousand back-packers stamping around the country during August and the murderer gets two of them. More than that will be run over crossing the street in less than a week.'

'True, no doubt,' said the inspector, 'but I would prefer not to cite the statistics in an unsolved report to the commissioner. They might not be regarded as an adequate explanation by the press.'

The media were by now in full cry and their comments on the police and gendarmerie efforts were not uniformly flattering.

'We've done everything we could,' said the sergeant resignedly. 'There's nothing now except to wait.'

Unfortunately for the nerves of the investigators, the wait was long. The first three weeks of August passed without a single report of any homicide which bore the trademark of the Back-packer Murderer. There were plenty of other murders and August was far from a holiday month for police and gendarmerie, but there were no pointless killings of young men in sleeping-bags.

'He's dead!' rejoiced the sergeant. 'Probably been run over by a lorry. There's only four days left to August. Back-packers are already getting scarce.'

It was true. With the nearing of the end of the holiday month, many of the back-packers and hitch-hikers had gone home to prepare for whatever awaited them there: school, a job or a search for one.

It was also true that the case might have ended in the death or crippling of the murderer. He was obviously moving around France a good deal in the summertime and his chances of being killed in a traffic accident were far higher than his victims' chances of being murdered.

The inspector was less optimistic. Normally, he was more so than the sergeant, but this time he was troubled by a sort of premonition that they had not heard the last of the Back-packer Murderer yet. It was the sort of feeling that he had had before and it had usually proved to be accurate.

It would prove to be this time too. The inspector and the sergeant had had their conversation on the afternoon of 27 August 1982. It was a Friday and they would

70

soon be going off duty for the weekend. Circumstances permitting, they did not work on Saturdays or Sundays.

It seemed that circumstances would permit. Nothing of urgency came in during the rest of the afternoon and they went home still wary, but largely relieved. By Monday, there would be only two days left to August and the Back-packer Murderer would have to work overtime if he hoped to get in his usual quota for the month. Even the inspector did not think he could do it.

That evening, as the inspector and the sergeant were peacefully watching television in their respective living rooms, a nineteen-year-old youth named Charles Petit was dozing off happily in his sleeping-bag, spread out in a high meadow of the Jura Mountains near Beaufort on the eastern border of France. An unemployed carpenter's mate, he was back-packing slowly down the length of France to his parents' home in Nice.

He would get there, but not by back-packing. Charles Petit would come home in a sealed coffin by rail.

For, at a little before midnight, not long after the inspector and the sergeant had switched off their television sets and gone to bed, a dark form moved silently across the meadow lit only by the glory of a million stars, bent over the sleeper and, an instant later, the quiet of the summer night was split by the vicious crack of a 7.65 mm pistol, fired twice in quick succession.

The body of the dead boy jerked reflexively and lay still.

The Back-packer Murderer had claimed his fifth victim and, despite the optimism of the investigators, he was going to meet his August quota after all.

The inspector and the sergeant knew nothing of this, however, and spent their weekend tranquilly. The body was not discovered until Monday morning.

Later, it was possible to determine that, while the inspector and the sergeant had been crossing France from west to east to the scene of the Charles Petit murder, the murderer had been crossing France from east to west from the scene of the Charles Petit murder to the scene of his final performance near the city of Bordeaux on the Atlantic coast.

He barely made it under the wire. It was just short of midnight on 31 August 1982 when the killer bent over another sleeping-bag and fired four shots from his 7.65 mm pistol through the head of twenty-six-year-old Konrad Mayer, an electrical engineer who came from the village of Werlte near Oldenburg, Germany.

Perhaps it was because he was hurrying to get in his yearly quota of murders before the end of the month or, perhaps, the routine of repetition had made him careless, but the Mayer murder was not quite as flawless as the others. Once again, the Back-packer Murderer stole his victim's ID card, an extremely foolish thing to do as Mayer was not only not French, but looked German, being big, burly and blond.

He did not steal any money, although Mayer had a good deal more with him than the other victims had had. A seasoned hiker who regarded back-packing as a sport, he had set off three weeks earlier to back-pack through the north of Italy and the south of France, and from Bordeaux would have been going home. His death was particularly tragic as he was the third of four sons to die a violent death, although the other two had been accidental.

Mayer's body was discovered early in the morning of 1 September and Inspector Descroix and Sergeant Saint, who had found nothing of value at the scene of the Charles Petit killing, went racing back across the country on the same day, harassed and, to say the least, dismayed.

But not despairing. Informed over the gendarmerie radio of the short length of time between the murder and the discovery of the body and the fact that the victim's ID card appeared to be missing, the inspector ordered that road-blocks be immediately set up in the area around the city. The case had now taken on such importance that every means available was at his disposal.

Police cars from Bordeaux and communities nearby poured into the area. Inspector and sergeant were still on their way to the scene when an arrest was made.

It was something of an anticlimax. A patrol car watching for stolen vehicles had stopped an elderly Renault R-4 bearing one of the licence numbers they were looking for. It was driven by a frail, hollow-cheeked young man whom they had asked for his identification.

Incredibly, the man had offered them the ID card of Konrad Mayer!

'But this isn't your identification card!' exclaimed the patrolman, too astonished to comprehend that this was precisely what half France was looking for.

The young man's teeth began to chatter. He had turned pale and looked as if he were about to faint. 'I'm a murderer! I'm a murderer!' he whispered in a trembling, barely audible voice.

And so he was. A timid, frightened murderer. The dreaded Back-packer Murderer was a twenty-one-year-old commercial artist who looked like the 'before' illustration for a body-building course, and the deadly 7.65 mm pistol with which he had ruthlessly executed his victims was found in his car. Ballistics tests would show it to have been the murder weapon in all six cases.

What neither ballistics nor any other kind of tests could show was why Pascal Bertrand had pulled the trigger a total of twelve times.

Bertrand, who came from the town of Stiring-Wendel in Lorraine, said first that he had killed the six young men because they were trying to rob him.

When it was pointed out that they had all been asleep at the time and that a sleeping-bag was an unusual place to stage a robbery, he changed his story and said he had shot them in self-defence when they attacked him. He was unable to say why they had attacked him or how they had managed this while asleep in a sleeping-bag.

As a matter of fact, Pascal Bertrand's explanation of the murders was not very plausible or even rational. A better explanation was offered by persons in Stiring-Wendel who had known him. They said he was crazy.

Such oversimplification is not for professional psychologists, of course. Of the many who observed Pascal Bertrand, some said that he was suffering from an inferiority complex; some that he was suffering from a superiority complex; others that his parents had failed him; that he was homosexual and had no luck with the boys; that he was heterosexual and had no luck with the girls; that he was bisexual and had no luck with either; and, of course, that he was a victim of the rotten, capitalist society, although, with the exception of Konrad Mayer, he was more affluent than any of his victims.

In one respect they agreed. He was dangerous and, if he was returned to society, it was probable that he would once again begin reducing its numbers.

He was, therefore, put quietly away in an institution, where he provides fascinating subject-matter for any number of scholarly studies and experiments in applied psychology.

And there he will remain.

Until someone comes to the conclusion that he has been cured.

6

THE GAMES GIRLS PLAY

The man standing in the charge room of the small police headquarters building in Dierdorf does not look very dangerous.

He is a short man, stockily built and hard-muscled, and, although his clean-shaven face is drawn with stress, it still bears the innocent, slightly wondering expression of the near-eastern peasant in unfamiliar surroundings.

The surroundings are not really unfamiliar. Bekaddin Bagci has spent nearly a third of his thirty years in West Germany and most of that in Dierdorf.

Even so, he speaks very little German. He does not come from a background where language skills are emphasized. For his ancestors, scratching a living out of the hard soil of Anatolia was more important than attending school, even if there were one for poor peasants in that little farming village to the south of the Turkish capital of Ankara.

Now, however, this lack of German is causing him trouble for he is trying to tell the duty sergeant something, and the duty sergeant does not speak Turkish.

Finally, the frustrated guest worker smiles apologetically, reaches over the charge desk and takes the startled sergeant by the throat with both hands.

He does not squeeze hard, but his hands are rough with manual labour and very muscular.

The sergeant reaches for his service pistol.

'Great marvel he didn't shoot him,' said Sergeant of

Detectives Klaus Berger. 'For all he knew, the fellow was as crazy as a cuckoo clock.'

'Probably couldn't get the safety catch off his gun,' said Inspector Hans Krupp, the sergeant's superior. 'Not much practice with a gun in a place like Dierdorf.'

Neither the inspector nor the sergeant were attached to the Dierdorf police, which is a modest enough organization as the village has less than five thousand inhabitants.

It was possible that there was a touch of sour grapes in the inspector's remark. Dierdorf is a quiet and lovely community snuggled into the green forest of the Westerwald. Koblenz, fourteen miles to the south, where the inspector lived, is a busy, polluted town at the junction of the Rhine and Mosel rivers. It is not, however, large, the population being under a hundred and twenty thousand.

The inspector and the sergeant had been summoned to Dierdorf because a murder had taken place there and they were the permanent members of the rural homicide squad. Villages like Dierdorf had no homicide squad and, sometimes, no criminal investigations department. It was more practical to handle such matters from the larger city with its better facilities.

As a rule, the rural homicide squad did not have a great deal to do. The Palatinate district to the west of the Rhine is mainly agricultural and lacks the large urban centres which generate so much violent crime. When a murder did take place, it was usually easy to solve as the identity of the murderer was obvious, even if he or she had not immediately come to the police to confess. The main task of the homicide squad then consisted of establishing the circumstances so that the appropriate charge could be brought at the trial.

The charge was rarely murder. Almost exclusively concerned with the rights of the accused, the German judicial system imposes so many conditions for a murder charge that the accused would have to carry out his crime

76

with the Criminal Code in one hand to make certain that he did not inadvertently provide the court with some excuse to reduce the charge to manslaughter.

The inspector was not anticipating any particular problem with this case. The chief of the Dierdorf police had telephoned to say that a Turkish guest worker had strangled his wife and come in to the station to report it. As he had been unable to make the duty sergeant understand what he wanted to report, he had demonstrated on the sergeant's neck and nearly got himself shot for his pains.

After the misunderstanding at the station had been cleared up, a team of officers went with the Turk to his third-floor apartment at 17 Ziegelei Strasse and reported back that the nude corpse of a young woman was lying on the floor of the living room. She had been dead for some time and, as her pubic area was depilated, they assumed that she was Turkish.

Nobody in the Dierdorf police spoke Turkish, but everybody knew that Turkish women removed their body hair.

One of the officers remained to guard the apartment and the other returned to police headquarters with the Turk, who was put in the detention cells.

This was clearly a matter for the rural homicide unit and the inspector and sergeant had set out immediately for Dierdorf, bringing with them the department's medical expert, Dr Leopold Finkbinder, a small, meticulous man with such a huge, curving moustache that he looked like a water buffalo about to charge.

The doctor was now examining the body and the inspector and sergeant were wandering aimlessly about the remarkably clean and tidy two-bedroom apartment, looking for nothing in particular and finding it. When the doctor had finished, they would pick up the Turk and take him to Koblenz, where an interpreter would be available for him to make his confession.

'Apparently liked loose clothing,' remarked the

sergeant, picking up an enormous pair of split-crotch lace panties from a chair near the living-room door. 'Either she imported them from Turkey or she had them tailor-made. You couldn't buy something this size in a shop.'

'And she couldn't have worn it either,' said the inspector. 'She'd have fallen through the thing. It wouldn't be a tight fit on a hippopotamus.'

'Well, then . . . ?' said the sergeant. He was a tousle-headed, dark-blond man in his late twenties with a wide mouth and a turned-up nose. He did not look very serious and the inspector privately thought him amusing.

'Then there was someone else here,' said the inspector. 'The fellow – what's his name? Baggy?'

'Bagci,' said the sergeant, consulting the first information report form which he had picked up at the Dier-dorf station. 'Bekaddin Bagci.'

'Easier to pronounce than most,' said the inspector. 'Well, Bagci must have got himself a queen-size girl friend. German maybe. I doubt that the Turks grow them this big. Anyway, this here is his wife and she didn't like the idea so he strangled her.'

'Sounds logical,' said the sergeant. 'About the same as Germans. The only difference is we'll have to have the confession translated.'

The doctor had now completed his work at the scene and reported that the woman, presumed to be Mrs Bagci, had been strangled to death manually at around three or four o'clock of that same morning. She had been punched in the face several times, but not very hard. Otherwise, there were no injuries. She had apparently not attempted to defend herself, for he could find no traces of skin or hair under her fingernails.

'Her final moments were not entirely unhappy,' concluded the doctor. 'The indications are that she was in a state of intense sexual excitement at the time of her death.'

The sergeant looked questioningly at the inspector.

78

The victim being in a state of sexual excitement at the time of the murder did not tie in very well with the theory they had just been discussing.

The inspector looked thoughtful. He was a large, well-nourished man, carefully groomed and with a smooth, bland, rather expressionless face.

'Maybe this isn't Mrs Bagci after all,' he said finally.

But it was. Mrs Zuheylan Bagci, aged twenty-six and, since 8 July 1977, wife of Bekaddin Bagci, factory worker, resident in Dierdorf at 17 Ziegelei Strasse.

That was about all that Bekaddin Bagci was prepared to reveal in his confession, which had been duly made and translated. Other than that his wife was an angel and he was very, very sorry that he had killed her. He had, he said, lost his temper.

Over what, he would not say. Nor would he comment on the giant split-crotch panties in his living room. When questioned, he merely looked blank and did not reply.

In the meantime, the autopsy of the corpse of Zuheylan Bagci had been carried out and Dr Finkbinder confirmed his original impression that the victim had been engaged in sexual activities on a level which he thought near the limit of human endurance. In his opinion, Mrs Bagci had been suffering from an extreme case of nymphomania.

The inspector found himself faced with a very puzzling case, for the doctor had also stated in the autopsy report that he had recovered no trace of semen in or on the body, but a great many traces of saliva which stemmed from at least two persons.

The conclusion was obvious: Mrs Bagci had been engaged exclusively in oral sex prior to her death.

What was not obvious was with whom.

Presumably, with Mr Bagci and the owner of the tent-like panties, but who was this person and what had gone wrong with what now looked like a three-way sex party?

In modern, emancipated Germany, sex parties are not uncommon, even in a place like Dierdorf, and it is not uncommon either for them to end in homicide. Since the media proclaimed the sexual revolution a few years earlier, many middle-class and middle-aged Germans were giving group sex a try and discovering that, media to the contrary, sexual jealousy continued to exist.

'But these were not Germans,' said the inspector irritably. 'Did you ever hear of guest workers going in for this sort of thing? They're too conservative.'

'The Bagcis have been here a long time,' said the sergeant. 'Maybe they became integrated. You want to see the background report?'

The inspector did. It was actually a composite report made up from several sources, including interviews with relatives of Bekaddin Bagci and his late wife, from which the sergeant had extracted the salient facts.

Zuheylan, it seemed, was also a long-time resident of Dierdorf, having gone to work in a factory there at the age of sixteen.

She and Bekaddin, who worked in another factory, had actually met in Dierdorf, although they both came from the same village in Turkey.

The wedding had been celebrated in Turkey and Bekaddin had been the envy of the bachelors of the village, as Zuheylan was not only very pretty and magnificently built, but was considered to be intelligent and a good housekeeper.

This last could be confirmed by the police personally. They had examined the spic and span apartment, which building superintendent Oscar Hellmich said was kept permanently in that state. The Bagcis, he asserted in his statement to the police, had been excellent tenants, being quiet, clean and having few visitors. Asked about sex parties, he expressed great doubt that there had been any.

Had it not been for the evidence uncovered by the autopsy, the police would have been inclined to doubt it also. The Bagcis had known everybody in the Turkish community, of course, but they had had no close friends and, although Mrs Bagci had spoken reasonably good German, her husband's lack of the language practically eliminated any possibility of social contact with the local inhabitants, little inclined to mix with the guest workers in any case.

Following the wedding in Turkey, the couple had returned to Dierdorf and continued with their factory jobs. From that time until the morning following the murder on 17 December 1979, only two incidents appeared in the record.

On 4 March 1978, Zuheylan Bagci had been admitted to the Dierdorf hospital for treatment of bruises and scratches on her face, hands and breasts. They were not serious and, following treatment, she was sent home.

And, on 1 February 1979, Bekaddin Bagci had lost his job at the factory. Since that date, he had been taking unofficial odd jobs, but the bulk of the family income was being provided by Zuheylan, who was still working.

'There is obviously something missing here,' said the inspector, handing the background report back to the sergeant. 'If this is all there is, there was no reason for Bagci to kill his wife and she must, therefore, still be alive.'

He was a man given to carrying logic to illogical lengths.

'Maybe there was,' said the sergeant. 'You recall Finkbinder's report on Bagci's physical examination? The man must have been half-mad from sheer frustration.'

Bekaddin Bagci having been formally indicted for the murder of his wife, the police could carry out an examination of him with or without his consent. But he had, as a matter of fact, cooperated willingly – as, indeed, he did in all phases of the investigation that did not touch on his motives for the murder.

According to Dr Finkbinder, Bagci was a sexual bomb on the verge of exploding. A healthy, normal man in the prime of life, he had, said the doctor, not obtained any form of sexual relief in months.

The inspector had found this a little hard to swallow, but the doctor's statement had been confirmed by none other than Bagci himself. No, he had told the inspector, he had not had intercourse with his wife for nearly two months and he could not go to a prostitute because he was a married man.

'And this is the fellow who was supposed to have been holding sex orgies in his apartment?' said the inspector. 'The further we get into this case, the stranger it is. But you're right: Bagci must have been under tremendous pressure, living with a beautiful, oversexed wife with whom he could not, for some reason or other, have intercourse. Maybe it has something to do with the woman with the monstrous underwear.'

'I think so,' said the sergeant, 'and I've got every man available trying to identify her. It's almost certain that she isn't Turkish. I've check ed the entire community in Dierdorf and there isn't a woman among them to fit those pants.'

'Shouldn't be many in the German community either, I would think,' said the inspector. 'If any detective ever had a fat lead to investigate, you do.'

The inspector's manner might be facetious, but it did not mean that he failed to regard the case seriously. He was a conscientious man and, for Bekaddin Bagci, a great deal depended upon the results of the investigation.

As things now stood, he would be tried on a charge of murder and, as he had confessed and showed no inclination to retract his confession, he would be convicted and given a heavy sentence, especially as there were no known extenuating circumstances.

Of course, if Bagci had ruthlessly murdered his wife over some triviality, he deserved a heavy sentence, but that was not the impression that the inspector had gained during the course of their interviews. Rather, he thought him a simple, sober sort of man with no tendency to violence who had been subjected to greater pressure than

82

he could bear. There was no doubting his sincere sorrow over the death of his wife.

Although he could not convince Bagci of it, it was vitally important to determine what that pressure had been for the German Criminal Code stated:

> If the slayer through no fault of his or her own was incited to rage through mistreatment or grave insult to him or her self or a dependent person and, thereby, lost control of his or her faculties of judgement or if there were other mitigating circumstances, the charge shall be manslaughter and the sentence may range from six months' to a maximum of five years' imprisonment.

The difference was, therefore, between five years maximum and a possible life sentence, although a full life sentence is almost never served in Germany today, with the possible exception of persons convicted of crimes involving money.

There was no money in this case, but there was the very large clue remarked upon by the inspector, and the sergeant spared no effort to uncover the identity of its owner, whom, he thought, he could recognize on sight.

The first thing he was able to determine was that the panties had not been purchased in Dierdorf. No shop there carried such a size and some of the shop owners expressed disbelief that such a size existed.

It did, however, and the sergeant was eventually able to determine that such remarkable garments were sold mostly by mail-order houses specializing in sex toys, pornography and other modern forms of entertainment.

He was not able to locate the mail-order house which had sold this particular garment and it appeared probable that it had gone out of business. So many people had entered the field following the sexual revolution that the market was not sufficiently large to support all of them.

Having failed here, the sergeant set his men to

canvassing the neighbourhood of the Bagci apartment house. The woman had definitely been in the building, as she had left her pants there. Perhaps someone had seen her and knew who she was.

In one of the oversights which so often plague criminal investigations, the sergeant failed to question the building superintendent, Oscar Hellmich. Hellmich had already made a statement to the police and the sergeant assumed that, if he had not made any mention of fat women in the building at that time, it was because he had not known of any.

Fortunately, Hellmich learned of the police canvass and the object of it and came voluntarily to the Dierdorf police station to report that he knew of a fat woman who had often visited the building and could, for all he knew, have been visiting the Bagcis. He did not keep very careful track of who came and went as this was not included in his duties.

In any case, he said, the woman was not all that fat. She was a fine figure of a woman and no frail slip of a girl, but there were others fatter than she. Her name, he added almost casually, was Berta Schlupper and she could often be found at a local bar called the Pink Pussy.

The information astounded the sergeant, who had now spent enough time snooping around Dierdorf to know what the Pink Pussy Tavern was.

It was a purely homosexual hangout, and not just any homosexuals, but exclusively female ones, although not all of the patrons would have agreed to this definition of their gender.

'What in heaven's name does that mean?' said the sergeant. 'I've asked around and this Berta Schlupper is a notorious lesbian, but what were her pants doing in the Bagci apartment?'

'She sure as hell wasn't visiting Bagci,' said the inspector. 'Mrs Bagci must have been a lesbian and, if she was, that explains a lot of things.'

'Such as why Bagci was married to a beautiful, over-

84

sexed wife and hadn't had sex for two months,' said the sergeant.

'And why Mrs Bagci was in a state of extreme sexual excitement at the time of her death, but without a trace of semen on her,' said the inspector.

'And even why Bagci won't discuss the motive for the murder,' said the sergeant. 'He's ashamed. Probably looks on female homosexuality as something perverted.'

'Well, it is,' said the inspector mildly. 'You can't maintain that it's normal. He probably came home unexpectedly and caught them red-handed. Berta took off, leaving her pants, and Bagci was so outraged and amazed that he punched his wife around a couple of times and then strangled her to death. Comes clearly under the manslaughter provisions of the code. He should get off with three or four years.'

'If we can prove it,' said the sergeant. 'I wouldn't think that Miss Schlupper would be anxious to testify in court that she was having an affair with Bagci's wife.'

But the sergeant was wrong. Thirty-eight-year-old Berta Schlupper was not in the least embarrassed at testifying to her homosexual relationship with Zuheylan Bagci, neither to the police nor later before the court. As she said, everyone she knew was aware that she was a lesbian, anyway.

Despite the impressive size of her underwear, Miss Schlupper was not an unattractive woman and she had been, she boasted, the Turkish woman's preferred partner.

Not, however, her only partner. According to Miss Schlupper and another lesbian, thirty-year-old Monika Fischbach, who also described herself as Zuheylan's preferred partner, the lovely Turk had been insatiable in her lust for love.

But only the love of women. Sex relations with men she found disgusting, and this included her husband.

This was only logical because Zuheylan considered herself to be a man and invariably took the male role in her relations with Berta, Monika and a good many others.

Her sexual preferences had been established as a child as far back as she could remember. She had had female lovers before she even met Bekaddin.

She had liked him in a man-to-man sort of way as long as they were not married, but had vigorously discouraged his courtship.

Bekaddin, who had taken this for commendable maidenly reserve, had gone to ask for her hand from her father, who, having investigated Bekaddin's background and work record, had granted it and had quite simply ordered his daughter to marry him.

Zuheylan might be unconventional in her sexual preferences, but disobedience to her father was out of the question and she had married, reluctantly and with great misgivings.

The misgivings were fully justified. Bekaddin's torment had begun on his wedding night when his wife ate an apple and thumbed through a magazine while he was engaged in making love to her.

And this was only the beginning. The relationship between the couple had got steadily worse and Zuheylan was soon refusing her husband his marital rights for months on end.

She had continued with her homosexual activities, becoming increasingly more blatant as her feelings of friendship toward Bekaddin passed from indifference through dislike to hatred.

She had taken to bringing her lesbian lovers home with her and engaging in sex with them in the very presence of her husband. After he had lost his job and was partially dependent upon her financially, she sometimes forced him to sleep on a cot in the kitchen while she shared the bed with her lover.

Bekaddin had stormed and threatened, but to no avail. He did not understand what was wrong with his wife and held the German women responsible for seducing

86

her. Hopelessly in love, he could not accept that Zuheylan actively preferred women partners to himself.

There had been terrible quarrels, but Bekaddin had never beaten Zuheylan. The time that she had been admitted to the hospital, her injuries were due to a scuffle among lesbians to determine who really was her preferred partner.

The matter had not been settled. Zuheylan could not be true to a single partner because the fire that burned in her was too strong for any single person, man or woman.

On the night of the murder, according to Berta Schlupper, Zuheylan promised her husband that she would come home by midnight and allow him his ration of sex. It had been six weeks since their last encounter.

Zuheylan, however, did not keep her promise and spent the night with two lesbians, leaving them both exhausted. She then sought out Berta and asked her to accompany her home as she was not yet sated and she could hope for no satisfaction from her husband.

Berta came. She knew Bekaddin and had actually lived for a time in the apartment with the Bagcis, until the quarrels had became too much for her.

Zuheylan assured her there would be no quarrel that night or, rather, that morning as it was by now nearly four o'clock.

They went to the apartment and found Bekaddin asleep in the bedroom, but he awakened when Zuheylan went in to take off her clothes and hang them up. She was a woman of tidy habits.

Berta remained in the living room and removed her underwear. She knew Zuheylan to be impetuous and she did not want it torn off.

Zuheylan returned to the living room, with Bekaddin following her. As Berta spoke no Turkish she did not know what they said, but Bekaddin was so vehement that she became nervous. He was, she thought, losing his mind and she had never before seen him in such a state.

Without stopping to pick up her pants, she ran out of the apartment and down the stairs. Even from the hall below, she could hear the voices of the raging Turks.

She had, she said, not been at all surprised when she learned that Bekaddin had murdered Zuheylan. It was something which everyone knew was sure to happen sooner or later.

Bekaddin Bagci confirmed generally the testimony of Berta Schlupper and the other lesbian lovers of his wife, but insisted that it was they who were entirely to blame. His wife, he wept, had been an innocent angel.

Whether she had been an angel previously, she was, presumably, one now, and the responsibility for her apotheosis lay with Bekaddin Bagci.

It was a responsibility which Bagci did not deny and one which the court could not ignore completely. Although sympathy for the tormented Turk was great, he was found guilty of manslaughter and, on 21 November 1980, sentenced to four and a half years' imprisonment.

The sentence was not appealed and he did not appear to regard it as too harsh.

Said Bekaddin Bagci, good Mohammedan, 'I fear God and I fear those women.'

7

MAKING A NEW START

Definitions are tiresome and often not very satisfactory, but it may be necessary to define what 'deviate' is.

The common understanding of the term is a person who is sexually abnormal, although it is becoming increasingly difficult to say precisely what abnormal is. There have been some outstanding experts in the field of psychology who maintain that nothing is sexually abnormal, which leads to the dubious proposition that a man who must disembowel his partner in order to achieve sexual satisfaction is behaving normally.

Many would think not, but what about bizarre actions which are not connected with sex? Is a person whose behaviour is so abnormal that few or none can understand it a deviate?

A difficult question and one which would no doubt give rise to controversy in some quarters.

It might be said that such persons were not deviates, but insane.

But there are persons who are not insane and know perfectly well what they are doing whose behaviour is still unintelligible to most or all of us.

Are they deviates?

The general definition is tedious, specific cases perhaps less so. So it may prove instructive to ponder the behaviour of the remarkable Mr Raupach, whose actions were rational and intelligible, but whose motives were not.

Or perhaps they were. No one knows what Mr

Raupach had in mind on that summer morning of 1983, apparently not even Mr Raupach.

It was a Friday, 8 July, and Heinz-Dietmar Raupach, a thirty-six-year-old employee of the Dresden Bank in the West German city of Frankfurt am Main, having pressed a husbandly kiss on his wife, said, 'Take care. See you this evening,' and departed in his beloved yellow Mercedes 280S for work. The time was shortly before eight.

As this was what Heinz-Dietmar said and did every morning of the week, Mrs Monika Raupach was not unduly impressed. An attractive, religious woman of thirty-three, she was the mother of two fine children, aged ten and eleven, and she worked half days at a local delicatessen. She and Heinz-Dietmar had been married since 5 April 1969 and she regarded her marriage as successful and happy. There were no financial problems. The total family income was fully adequate to provide for a comfortable scale of living.

There had, of course, been a little disturbance three years earlier when Heinz-Dietmar had confessed that he was having an affair with one of the neighbours, but he had vigorously rejected her offer of a divorce and she assumed that the matter had been laid to rest. She had not understood Heinz-Dietmar's misstep very well. She knew the neighbour and she was not only less attractive than herself, but fifteen years older to boot. Heinz-Dietmar, she thought, could have done better if he had set his mind to it.

None of these thoughts crossed the mind of Monika Raupach on that July morning. The matter had long since been settled and required no further thought. If Heinz-Dietmar sometimes showed a tendency to stray from the path of marital righteousness, well, the church did not approve, but, after all, they had been married for nearly fifteen years and, anyway, half the married men in Dietzenbach had a little something going on the side.

Monika Raupach, therefore, went cheerfully about her usual duties, working until noon at the delicatessen, preparing lunch for the children and then getting on with the afternoon's housework.

It was a little after three o'clock when she noticed that her husband's summer suits were not hanging in the wardrobe.

Monika found this strange, and she found it stranger still when she discovered that Heinz-Dietmar's suitcases, the ones which he always took on holiday, were also missing.

Troubled by a growing premonition, Monika checked the drawer in the living room where the family papers were kept.

Heinz-Dietmar's personal identity card and his passport were not there.

Monika Raupach laid down her duster and picked up the telephone. She dialled the number of her husband's office with a heart that was beginning to beat a little more rapidly than usual.

The news from the office did nothing to slow it. Mr Raupach was not there. He was gone for three weeks' holiday.

Monika Raupach's next call was to Pieta Schreiber. She did not, however, expect an answer. Mrs Schreiber was the forty-eight-year-old neighbour with whom Heinz-Dietmar had been diverting himself three years earlier.

To her astonishment, Pieta Schreiber was at home. No, she had not seen Heinz-Dietmar. No, she did not know where he was. And, what was more, she did not care. Click of broken connection.

Monika Raupach sat down weakly on the sofa. Something had happened with Heinz-Dietmar, but what? Had he left her? Was he with another woman? What was the matter with the man?

After a time it occurred to her that her husband had only gone on three weeks' vacation and that he would have to return then or lose his job. In three weeks she would know. She was a patient woman. She could wait.

It was, however, five days short of a month before Monika next heard from Heinz-Dietmar, and it was not because he had returned from holiday, but because he had written her a letter.

There was no return address on it, but it was postmarked Innsbruck, Austria, and it had been mailed on 1 August.

It was not really a letter, but a sort of farewell note. In it, he said that Monika would never see him again. He was planning to commit suicide.

Monika did not know what to do. She did not think that planning to commit suicide was a violation of the law, so there was no point in going to the police. In the end, she went to the pastor of her church, who did not know what to do either, but comforted her with the assurance that things would be better in the next world.

Monika was not, however, going to get to the next world as quickly as her husband for, three days later, on the night of 6 August, a twenty-year-old motorcycle rider named Peter Funk came roaring up to the headquarters of the Innsbruck gendarmerie to report that there was a car off the road near the village of Tulfes and it was burning like a torch.

A gendarmerie rescue squad set off immediately, although the time was two-thirty in the morning. During the months of July and August, the main road leading down from Germany through Innsbruck to the Brenner Pass is bumper to bumper with cars, and accidents take place round the clock.

The scene of this accident was not, however, the main road, but an isolated, very winding, secondary road which led from the small village of Hall to the smaller village of Tulfes. Five hundred yards from the point where the road entered Tulfes, there was a hairpin bend with a grassy slope below. A hundred and fifty yards down the slope stood a car which, even by the time that the gendarmerie party reached the scene, was still burning in a solid column of flame.

There was, of course, nothing that the gendarmes could do about it. Through the flames and smoke, they could see what appeared to be a human form behind the steering wheel, but anyone in the car would be long since dead. All that remained was to wait until the fire had burned itself out and then attempt to identify the victim.

That proved to be not too difficult. The car was a 1977 yellow Mercedes 280S with the German licence plate number OF-DR515 and, as German licence numbers indicate the locality in which the car is registered, a single telephone call was enough to determine that it had been the property of Heinz-Dietmar Raupach.

'Had been' because there was less remaining of Heinz-Dietmar than of the car. He was as thoroughly cooked as a barbecued pig, a blackened crust covering the medium to well-done flesh beneath. Nothing could be discerned, neither features, fingers nor anything that protruded from what looked more like a carbonized log than a human body.

None the less, enough for an identification had survived. A small patch of medium-brown hair where Raupach's scalp had pressed against the headrest remained. A wedding ring with the inscription '*Monika. 5.4.69*' was on the stump of a finger. A key marked '*Dresden Bank*' was recovered from the floor, together with a size nine and a half shoe. And on the ground near the front of the car was a German Army T-shirt, later identified by Monika Raupach as a rag which her husband had kept in the car to wipe condensation off the windscreen.

The identification was completed and the body was shipped back to Dietzenbach in a sealed coffin. The widow was not permitted to view the corpse and wept copiously at the funeral, as did the children and other relatives of the deceased.

Heinz-Dietmar Raupach had, it seemed, carried out

his suicide threat. When the local police asked his wife to make a statement concerning what Raupach had been doing in Austria for the Innsbruck gendarmerie file, she showed them the suicide note, which they photocopied and sent along with the report.

They assumed that the report would close the gendarmerie case, but, in fact, it opened it. The gendarmes had been looking upon Raupach's death as an accident, and with good reason, for the autopsy had shown that the victim's blood had contained enough alcohol to pickle a horse.

This, in turn, explained how Raupach had managed to go off the road at a point where in the history of the gendarmerie, there had never before been an accident.

Going off the road at this point was actually rather difficult. The hairpin bend forced a driver to slow to a near crawl and, even if the vehicle did wander off the paving and on to the grassy slope beside it, bringing it back on to the road was a simple matter. There were tyre marks in the grass showing that this had happened on several occasions in the past.

The yellow Mercedes had, however, continued in a straight line down the slope, come to a stop and burst into flames. As far as could be determined, it had not struck anything and it had not turned over.

'Then, why did it catch fire?' said Captain Aldo Mueller.

The question was directed at Gendarmerie Sergeant Franz Gustl, a very large young man with short blond hair and, at the moment, a rather hang-dog expression. The sergeant had conducted the investigation into the accident which had taken the life of Heinz-Dietmar Raupach.

'The assumption was,' said the sergeant, 'that he was drunk and smoking a cigarette. He passed out after rounding the hairpin bend and the car rolled off the road and down the slope. The cigarette fell on his clothes or something else inflammable and set the car on fire.'

'Whose assumption?' said the captain. He was a hard-muscled, hard-jawed, hard-driving officer who was known to his subordinates as fair, but not easy.

'Well – uh – mine,' said the sergeant. 'And Dr Sacher's, of course.'

Dr Albert Sacher was the gendarmerie medical officer who had performed the autopsy on the corpse of Heinz-Dietmar Raupach.

'Tell Sacher I want to talk to him,' said the captain. 'And come back. I want you in on this too.'

The sergeant did as he was told and, as the doctor's office was on the floor below, returned very promptly. He did not know what was bothering the captain, but he had an uneasy feeling that he was going to be held responsible for something.

The doctor was troubled with no such feelings. A dark and hairy little man with a snappish manner, he seated himself on the arm of the chair in front of the captain's desk, pointed out that he had a great deal to do at this particular time of year and asked what the captain wanted.

The captain silently handed him the statement which the Dietzenbach police had taken from Mrs Raupach.

The doctor read it. 'Well?' he said, handing it back.

'It wasn't an accident,' said the captain, passing the statement on to the sergeant.

'So?' said the doctor. 'Change the entry on the death certificate to suicide. You can do that on receipt of additional information.'

'But was it suicide?' said the captain.

'It wasn't old age,' said the doctor. 'The man burned to death.'

'And he was so determined that he simply sat there and burned to death without making any attempt to get out of the car?' said the captain. 'Quite a demonstration of will-power. Or was he so drunk that he didn't even feel it?'

The doctor looked suddenly thoughtful, got up, walked around the chair and sat down in it.

'No,' he said. 'He wasn't that drunk. He had close to three parts in a thousand alcohol content in the bloodstream, but the man was German. Unless he was a real freak, he'd have built up a tolerance from swilling beer. He'd have felt the fire.'

'Do you think he'd have the strength to sit there and burn consciously?' said the captain.

'No,' said the doctor.

'My conclusion also,' said the captain. 'Sergeant Gustl, I want you to reopen the investigation into this case, and let's not go about it quite so light-heartedly this time. Dismiss.'

'Dismiss' meant get out, and the sergeant got out. But, after a decent interval of time, he returned to ask if the captain had anything specific in mind as to what he was supposed to investigate. He could not see that it made a great deal of difference whether Raupach had died as the result of an accident or whether he had killed himself.

'You might begin by trying to determine if this *was* Raupach,' said the captain. 'Contact the German police and see what he had in the way of insurance.'

'Holy cats!' said the sergeant in an awe-struck voice. 'You think he murdered somebody for the insurance!'

'I think there's something very funny about this accident or suicide or whatever it is,' said the captain. 'What was Raupach doing here in the first place? The Dietzenbach police said he was on holiday. Since when do people go on holiday to commit suicide? If the man was here, he had some reason to be here. Find out what it was.'

The sergeant had no idea how he was to do this, but he did not dare ask. After thinking the matter over a little and sending off a request to the Dietzenbach police for information on the late Heinz-Dietmar's financial circumstances and the height of his insurance policy, if any, he went out to the scene of the accident and walked around Tulfes, asking if anyone had seen a yellow Mercedes or if anyone there knew a German named Heinz-Dietmar Raupach.

To his surprise, a farmer named Walter Grumann said that he had seen a yellow Mercedes pass along the road at least twice within the past week. It was a rather conspicuous car.

Grumann seemed to be unusually observant and the sergeant took him into the local tavern, bought him a drink and questioned him about what else he might have noticed.

He had been doubtful as to whether he could safely include the drink on an expense voucher, but it turned out to be worth paying for himself.

Grumann said that he had not only seen the yellow Mercedes twice, but he had seen the driver of it in another car, a blue Volkswagen Rabbit with an Austrian licence plate. It had been moving slowly along the road to Hall, and on the evening of the accident he had seen it parked beyond the hairpin curve.

The sergeant was intrigued. Was he absolutely certain that it had been the same driver?

Absolutely, said Grumann. A big fellow, six feet or more, heavy built with brown hair. He had not looked like a local Austrian.

The sergeant did not ask what a local Austrian was supposed to look like, but hurried back to his office and sent off another request to the Dietzenbach police. He had seen Raupach only as a blackened stump. He wanted a picture of him as he had been alive.

The Dietzenbach police, somewhat puzzled by the Austrian gendarmerie's interest in a suicide victim, obtained a recent picture of Raupach from the widow and sent it down to Innsbruck.

Grumann recognized it immediately.

All of this took a little time, but, while waiting, the

sergeant had been busy and had identified the blue Volkswagen Rabbit.

He had guessed that it would be a rental car and it was. Raupach had rented it in Innsbruck on 4 August, using his own name, and had not yet returned it.

The sergeant did not inform the agency that the client was presumed dead and there was no telling what had happened to their car. Instead, he said that, if the client came to turn in the vehicle, they were to attempt to detain him and notify the gendarmerie at once.

The instructions to the agency were merely a precaution. The sergeant did not think that Raupach was liable to turn in the car. Wherever he had gone, he had taken it with him.

And, if there was no other reason to believe that Heinz-Dietmar Raupach was still alive, the missing Volkswagen was evidence enough.

It was, the sergeant thought, now fairly clear what had happened.

Raupach, probably with the collusion of his wife, had attempted an elaborate insurance swindle. Insured to the eyes, he had murdered someone resembling himself and had burned him up in the car. The blue Volkswagen had been the get-away vehicle to which he had transferred after torching the Mercedes. Back in Dietzenbach, the spurious widow was now happily collecting the insurance, and once things had quietened down a little, would be discreetly off to join her husband, risen, so to speak, from the dead.

Captain Mueller was impressed with this theory of the case and pointed out that it could also explain why Raupach's Army T-shirt had been found outside the car. Raupach had used it for a fuse after soaking the interior of the vehicle with petrol.

He immediately ordered a search of the missing-person reports for a six-foot-tall man with brown hair who had disappeared after 6 August with a view to identifying the victim, but the operation did not produce the anticipated results.

There was no missing-person report of a six-foot-tall man with brown hair for the period in question. Not in Austria. Not in Switzerland. Not in Italy. Not in Germany.

The police report from Dietzenbach did not improve matters.

Heinz-Dietmar had been insured for the trifling sum of three and a half thousand pounds. The car had not been insured at all and was not even completely paid for. There was still outstanding some three thousand pounds and, as Monika Raupach had co-signed for the credit, she was obliged to pay it.

That and another three thousand pounds in cheques which Heinz-Dietmar had written on their nearly empty joint account during the period 8 July to 6 August.

Monika Raupach was, without question, in dire financial straits and there was no way in which she or anyone else could have made a penny out of the death of her husband.

'It must have been Raupach after all,' said the captain. 'He didn't murder somebody. Somebody murdered him. That's why there's no missing-person report.'

'But it was Raupach who rented the Volkswagen,' said the sergeant. 'He had to show his ID card and licence.'

'No,' said the captain. 'It was somebody who looked like him. Raupach must already have been dead. The fellow was using his papers to cover the murder.'

'Sacher said the victim was burned to death in the car,' said the sergeant.

'Sacher must be wrong, or the murderer was maybe holding Raupach prisoner somewhere until he could complete his plans to burn him up,' said the captain.

'Why?' said the sergeant.

The captain opened his mouth, left it open for a moment and closed it again. 'You're right,' he said. 'There's no reason.'

There was more wrong with the case than a lack of motive. Where, for example, was the blue Volkswagen Rabbit now? Where had the murderer been holding Raupach until the time came to burn him up? How had he managed to keep him in the car and behind the wheel while he set fire to it? Dr Sacher was positive that the fire had been the cause of death and that there were no traces of any restraints on the victim's body.

Finally, what had Heinz-Dietmar had in mind when he ran off to Austria, wrote his wife a suicide note and issued three thousand pounds' worth of rubber cheques?

That, at least, could be investigated, for there was a record of where each cheque had been cashed. Whoever had cashed them would have been in contact with Raupach, for the bank in Dietzenbach was completely positive that the signatures on the cheques were his.

Raupach had moved around, it seemed. He had stayed in a sort of luxury tavern called the Bierwirt in the town of Amras, where he had been accompanied by an attractive young lady who could not now be located. He had stayed at the resort hotel Kupfer-Pfandl with a twenty-nine-year-old barmaid named Helena Kropski, who could be located, but who told the gendarmes that she had not even known her companion's first name. He had been a customer in the bar. He drove a yellow Mercedes with a German licence plate. He was generous and sexually not a freak. That was all.

Further cheques had been issued in Merano, Italy, and Athens, Greece. Heinz-Dietmar had had a weakness for luxury hotels and an aversion to sleeping alone in them.

'He certainly had a wonderful time before he got himself murdered,' remarked Captain Mueller, 'but he would have made things easier for us if he had kept a little of the money instead of spending all of it.'

Calculated on the basis of cheques cashed and sums spent, Heinz-Dietmar had had very little cash left at the time of his death, which fact effectively eliminated the captain's last hope of establishing any plausible motive.

Sergeant Gustl remained silent. Almost any theory that had been advanced or could be advanced had turned out to be full of holes, and he felt the less he said, the better.

'Nothing more we can do now,' continued the captain. 'We'll just have to wait until the Volkswagen turns up, if it ever does.'

The licence number of the rented Volkswagen had been turned over to Interpol, and, if it was found, it might be possible to pick up the trail from there.

Neither the captain nor the sergeant was very optimistic on this score. The driver would be heading south. He was, perhaps, by now in the Middle East or Africa.

But the gendarmes were mistaken. The blue Volkswagen was not heading south, but north, and on 29 September, Mrs Monika Raupach was summoned to the Dietzenbach police station.

'Mrs Raupach,' said the inspector who received her, 'I will be blunt. Your husband is alive.'

Monika Raupach stared at him with bulging eyes. 'I don't believe you!' she said weakly.

The inspector made a sign and a door leading to another office opened part way. Standing there was Heinz-Dietmar Raupach.

Monika staggered and clutched at the inspector for support.

'What does this mean, Heinz-Dietmar?' she blurted in a hoarse whisper. 'Are you coming back to us now?'

'Never,' said Heinz-Dietmar Raupach and closed the door.

Mrs Raupach fainted.

The inspector himself had nearly fainted when Raupach walked into the police station and calmly announced who he was. Having been kept abreast of the case by the Innsbruck gendarmerie, the Dietzenbach police believed Raupach to be dead.

That, it seemed, was what Raupach wanted everyone to believe and he had succeeded admirably. The plan for staging his own death had been perfect.

The only thing wrong with it was that it was pointless. Raupach gained nothing at all from his disappearance or from the murder.

For, as he admitted freely, it was murder. The body in the car was that of a casual drinking companion whom he picked up at the railway station bar in Innsbruck. He never knew his name or anything about him, but chose him simply because he was about his own size and appearance.

That the man had not been reported missing was not strange. European railway station bars are normally a social centre for lonely single men with neither family nor connections. If one disappears no one notices or cares.

Raupach said the murder had been committed in self-defence when the man attacked him. He gave him a karate chop and, seeing that it had killed him, became frightened and decided to fake an accident.

He was unable to explain how he had happened to rent the Volkswagen two days earlier and have it conveniently parked where he could leave with it after setting fire to the Mercedes.

In fact, Heinz-Dietmar was unable to explain any of his actions. He could not explain why he had so carefully plotted his disappearance. He could not explain why he had decided to return. He had simply been fed up with his life and had wanted a change, he said.

In that respect, he was successful. After a relatively short trial which left more questions unanswered than otherwise, Heinz-Dietmar was found guilty of the German judiciary's favourite charge of manslaughter. On 3 October 1984, he was sentenced to thirteen years in prison, where his life is totally different from what it was previously.

Monika Raupach obtained a divorce, returned the

insurance money and settled down to paying off her husband's debts, for which she was, of course, held legally responsible.

And nobody ever knew the name of the lonely man who had sought a little human warmth in the drab surroundings of a railway station bar and had been burned alive in Heinz-Dietmar's beloved Mercedes.

8

A SLIGHTLY TOO MERRY WIDOW

It was a fine high-summer morning on 25 January 1983 when twenty-five-year-old Christopher Enderly appeared at the central police station in Christchurch to report his mother missing.

With a population of under two hundred thousand, Christchurch is not a terribly large city, but it is the biggest on New Zealand's South Island, which is climatically cooler than North Island – the seasons and geography of the southern hemisphere are reversed.

Christopher, an assistant accountant with one of the city's commercial firms, was worried and he showed it. A well-spoken young man with a somewhat scruffy beard and rimless glasses, he said that his mother, fifty-one year-old Sarah Enderly, had not appeared for breakfast that morning and, when he went to look for her in her bedroom, she was not there and the bed had not been slept in. He was afraid that there might have been an accident. It was very unlike his mother to stay away from home overnight.

The duty sub-inspector asked a few details, assured him that the matter would be looked into and, after Enderly had departed for work, sent the first information report over to the missing persons section.

Mrs Enderly, it seemed, was a widow, and Christopher a half-orphan. His father, Gus Enderly, a merchant seaman, had been lost in a shipwreck in 1977.

Although Sarah and Christopher were in reasonably comfortable circumstances, the widow held a part-time job as a waitress at the university restaurant from four in the afternoon until eleven in the evening.

As she had apparently not come home on the preceding evening, a detective from the missing persons section went to the university restaurant to see if she had been at work and whether anyone knew where she might have gone.

He returned with the information that Mrs Enderly had worked her normal hours and had left at the usual time of eleven.

The detective then drove out to the Enderlys' home, a sprawling, elderly villa at 7 Oakdene Road on the outskirts of the city, to see if Mrs Enderly had, in the meantime, returned.

She had not, and the detective spent the rest of the day checking out accident reports and admissions to the city's hospitals and clinics.

Mrs Enderly was not in any of them and the matter began to take on a more alarming aspect. A recent picture of the missing woman was obtained from her son and police requests for information were run in the local newspapers.

No one reported having seen her, which was ominous. Although not precisely beautiful, Sarah Enderly had a face that was not easily forgotten.

The picture, described by her son as flattering, showed a woman with a deeply lined face, a sagging double chin, pouches under the eyes and too much make-up, who looked all of her age and, perhaps, a bit more.

And because of Mrs Enderly's age and appearance, the missing persons section was inclined to take the matter more seriously. This was no teenage girl who had run off on a romantic adventure. There was scarcely any explanation for the disappearance other than a criminal act.

In the end, the missing persons section came to the conclusion that the case was beyond their competence and turned it over to the department of criminal investigations. There it was taken up by Inspector Harold Baker, a jovial fair-haired man with a fine, upswept moustache, who promptly assigned it to his second-in-command, Detective Sergeant Walter Cruikshank.

The sergeant, a darkly scowling man with thick black brows, a chin blue with close-shaven beard and an expression of total distrust in everything and everyone, read through the first information report, the report on the investigations by the missing persons section, gazed thoughtfully at Mrs Enderly's picture and assigned two of his detectives to prepare a background report on the missing woman, something which had not, as yet, been done.

Two days passed and there was no report from the detectives. The sergeant called them in and asked if they had any plans to stop drinking beer and carry out their assignment.

The detectives replied that they had had no time for beer and would report on their assignment when it was completed. So far, they had traced about twenty men who had been romantically involved with Sarah Enderly, but they were of the opinion that this represented no more than the tip of the iceberg.

The sergeant was fascinated and demanded an immediate interim report.

For at least four years, said the detectives, Sarah Enderly had been leading a love life to cause women thirty years her junior to pale with envy. She had not managed a different partner every night, but she had not missed often.

'Are you sure you've got the right woman?' said the sergeant, picking the photo portrait from the file and examining it with new interest.

The detectives were certain. Mrs Enderly had been reasonably discreet in her affairs, but the sheer volume had attracted attention. Known as the Sexy Widow of Oakdene Road, she was mildly famous in some circles.

For a woman with so many sex partners, she lived an

orderly life, taking care of her housework in the morning and in the afternoon going for walks in the park, where she selected her bed companion for that evening after she came off work.

There had never been any difficulty in making contacts. She was widely known as an enthusiastic sex partner and, as the encounters took place in darkness, her appearance was not a serious handicap. She was, moreover, not very particular and, as she never charged for the entertainment, her popularity among the types of men who spent much of their time in the park was assured.

Having listened with considerable astonishment to all this, the sergeant told the detectives to continue with their investigation, concentrating on the more recent encounters, and took the file in to Inspector Baker. Mrs Enderly, he reported, had probably been murdered by one of her lovers.

The inspector read through the reports, looked at Mrs Enderly's photograph and said, 'Why?'

'No reason at all, perhaps,' said the sergeant. 'Homicidal maniac. Deviate of some kind. Obviously, if you're going to switch partners seven nights a week, sooner or later, you're sure to run into somebody special. The odds just ran out on her.'

'Weird,' said the inspector, studying the picture. 'Well, all right. Open a homicide investigation on it. You'll have to try and pick up the trail from the university restaurant on Monday evening. Where did she take them? Cheap hotels?'

'Home,' said the sergeant. 'She always took them home.'

But not, apparently, on the evening of 24 January. According to the other waitresses at the university restaurant, Sarah Enderly had not been accompanied on that evening.

Normally, there would have been a man waiting for her to come off work, and her colleagues had found it entertaining to speculate on what Sarah had dredged up for that night's tender romance. Some of the lovers, they said, had been beyond belief.

Where then had Sarah gone on that warm summer evening? Had she headed for the park or, perhaps, some cheap tavern hoping desperately to scratch up something even at that late hour. Or had she simply gone home?

The sergeant did not know how Mrs Enderly had travelled from and to work and he had to ask her son.

He did not like this very much as he was afraid the son might ask about the progress of the investigation and he was not certain how much Christopher knew about his mother's private life.

A superficial check run on him had shown that he was a remarkably wholesome type, a Rover Scout, and not at all the sort of son who would approve of his mother frolicking between the sheets with every bum she could drag out of the public parks.

Enderly did not, however, ask any questions other than whether the police had found any trace of his mother yet. He replied to the sergeant's query that his mother had always travelled by bus as she had no other means of transport. It was convenient, as the stop was at the end of Oakdene Road and only some thirty yards from the house.

This was good news. If Mrs Enderly had taken the bus every day, then the bus driver should know her by sight, at least, and be able to say whether she had been on the bus the evening of 24 January.

The sergeant did not expect that she would have been. Obviously, she had not come home on the bus because she had gone off somewhere with her murderer to be killed.

'But she did,' said the bus driver, Ralph Daniels. 'The same as every night. Eleven-thirty's my last trip and there aren't usually many passengers. There were three that evening and she was the last to get down.'

Daniels said he had known Sarah Enderly well and

had sometimes chatted with her when she was alone, which was not often. She had been alone on that evening and they had exchanged a few words. He knew her reputation, but thought she was a pleasant woman and that her sex life was her own business.

The sergeant's reaction to this was to investigate Ralph Daniels. At eleven-thirty in the evening, Oakdene Road would have been practically deserted. It seemed impossible that anything could have happened to Sarah Enderly in the thirty yards from the bus stop to her home.

Daniels was not, however, a very good suspect. He was only twenty-three, younger than Sarah's son, and, although no Romeo, quite attractive enough to have no problems with girls of his own age.

What could he have wanted from fifty-one-year-old Sarah Enderly? Sex? She would have been delighted. Money? She would have had scarcely more than the bus fare on her, according to her son.

Still, Daniels was the last person known to have seen Sarah and, the trip being the last of the day, he could have taken twenty minutes or half an hour before returning without anyone being the wiser.

He was never questioned directly about his time, so it was not known whether he could have provided an alibi or not. As it turned out, it did not matter.

At the time, there was no such thing as an alibi for no one knew what had happened to Sarah Enderly or whether anything at all had happened to her. She was inexplicably missing, but she could simply have been unusually taken with one of her lovers and gone off somewhere with him.

If she had, however, it was after having returned home on the bus that evening and without her clothes or personal items, for Christopher reported that none of her things were missing.

'In that case,' said Inspector Baker, 'she has to be somewhere between the bus stop at the end of Oakdene Road and her own house. Check out the other residents.'

The residents of the other houses along Oakdene Road were investigated and questioned. None could be regarded even remotely as having been involved in whatever had happened to Sarah Enderly.

They all knew her, of course, and they all knew her reputation. Most of them found her activities highly amusing, but a few expressed sympathy for Christopher, who, they thought, would suffer a shock if he ever found out what his mother was doing with her leisure time. All agreed that he did not know yet, and some apparently thought him rather a simpleton.

'We've talked to everybody out there,' said the sergeant, reporting to Inspector Baker, 'and we've had a look at the houses. No search warrants required. They were all ready to cooperate. There's nothing.'

'What about number nineteen?' said the inspector, scanning the list of interviews. 'You've got no names down against it.'

'That's because nobody lives there,' said the sergeant. 'It's up for sale and has been for a year or so.'

'Actually,' said the inspector in mild reproof, 'that's the first place you should have looked.'

Sarah Enderly – or rather her lifeless body – was not, however, in the empty house, but in the garden behind it. She lay face down in a luxuriant growth of weeds and the flies had been busy. Had she not been discovered then, she would have become noticeable to passers-by within a few more days.

Inspector Baker came out personally to view the corpse.

'Head injuries?' he asked Dr Peter Ambrose, the department's young and earnest medical officer, who was examining the body.

'Hammer, I should think,' said the doctor. 'Seven very violent blows, all to the back of the head. The last three or four were probably delivered after she had fallen down. A bit too much time has passed to be certain, but I suspect the initial attack didn't take place here.'

The doctor's opinion was shared by the technicians from the police laboratory, who thought that Mrs Enderly would have been struck down from behind while walking along the road in the direction of her home.

She had then been dragged into the yard of the empty house and hit several times more over the head to make certain that she was dead.

Why this had been done was a total mystery. The victim had not been sexually molested and her handbag lay two feet away from the body. It contained more money than her son had thought she would have been carrying, but it had not been opened. The fingerprints on it were, however, not hers.

Her gold wristwatch was still on her wrist and had stopped at twenty minutes past three. As there was no way of knowing when she had last wound it, the position of the hands was of no value in determining the time of death. Dr Ambrose estimated, however, that it had been the same evening as her disappearance.

Mrs Enderly wore jewellery to a very considerable value, but none of it had been taken and it was obvious that robbery was not a motive.

'Neither money nor sex,' mused the inspector. 'It doesn't leave much except complete insanity, but, if there is a madman running around killing people with a hammer, how is it that we have only this one case?'

A survey of other recent unsolved cases was carried out immediately following the discovery of the body on the theory that this might be a part of a series, but nothing remotely resembling the Enderly murder was found.

'Hatred?' suggested the sergeant. 'Revenge for some real or fancied wrong?'

'Possible,' said the inspector, 'but I find it hard to imagine the circumstances that would lead to such hatred. Who could an elderly, widowed waitress in the university restaurant have wronged so terribly that they would be prepared to murder her?'

'She had an unusual hobby,' argued the sergeant. 'Maybe she took some woman's man away.'

'Yes, a woman with a good hammer and a strong arm could have done it,' said the inspector, 'but you know the kind of men she associated with. Do you think any sane woman would have committed murder for one of them?'

'No,' said the sergeant, 'but that leaves nothing except a homicidal maniac who killed once and once only. If that's the case, we might as well write it off as unsolved now.'

'We may have to,' said the inspector, 'but before we do, I want every man she was with identified and investigated. When was he with her last? Where was he on the night of the murder? Has he ever been under psychiatric treatment or charged with a crime of violence? Let me know when you've finished.'

The sergeant's eyes bulged. 'You're not asking much, are you?' he said reproachfully. 'The woman's been changing partners practically every night for four years and you expect me to . . .!'

'Oh, it couldn't be all that bad,' said the inspector soothingly. 'This is not a large city. She must have had a good deal of repeat business.'

The sergeant was not comforted and, as there are few things which sharpen the wits more than the prospect of a monumental amount of tedious detail work, rapidly came up with half a dozen new theories of the crime, none of which were tenable.

He had given up and resigned himself to his fate when he was suddenly rescued by new information from an unexpected source.

Unexpected and, up until that time, unsuspected. The name of Roger Ackworth meant nothing to the sergeant when he was informed by the duty officer in the charge room that a gentlemen of that name was there and wished to speak to whoever was in charge of the Enderly murder investigation.

Technically, it was the inspector who was in charge, but the sergeant said that he would see him and Ackworth was sent up.

A dignified, well-dressed, well-groomed man in his fifties, the sergeant could not conceive of him as one of Sarah Enderly's lovers and, indeed, he was not.

Rather, he was the father of a very attractive twenty-three-year-old girl named Melanie and Melanie, it seemed, was a Queen's Guide.

Mr Ackworth spoke gravely and slowly, carefully choosing his words, and the sergeant, becoming a little impatient, demanded to know what this had to do with the Enderly murder.

'Christopher Enderly was engaged to marry my daughter,' said Ackworth. 'He is also active in the scouting movement and they met at a scouting function last summer.

'Melanie was very taken with him and we agreed to receive him at our home on the day before Christmas. He impressed us as a respectable young man and we raised no objections to an engagement.

'We were, perhaps, hasty in this decision and, when we looked more carefully into Mr Enderly's background, we found that he was, unfortunately and through no fault of his own, totally unsuitable as a husband for our daughter.

'We therefore asked her to return his ring and sever her relationship with him and she did so on 18 January.'

'And?' said the sergeant, puzzled.

'She told us that he was exceedingly bitter,' said Ackworth, 'and that he made threats against his mother's life. Something to the effect that she would either stop or he would stop her.'

'Stop what?' said the sergeant, intrigued but uncomprehending.

'Mrs Enderly was the reason for terminating our

daughter's engagement to her son,' said Ackworth. 'Our investigations showed that she was leading an incredibly dissolute life. Christopher was blameless, but we could not allow our family to be associated with a family in which there was such scandalous behaviour.'

'Someone who hated her bitterly,' murmured the sergeant. 'Someone she had terribly wronged . . .'

'I beg your pardon?' said Roger Ackworth.

'Nothing,' said the sergeant. 'I've just found a person I've been looking for.'

'We should have thought of the boy before,' said the inspector. 'We knew his character was the direct opposite to that of his mother.'

'We thought he didn't know,' said the sergeant, 'but it seems he'd known for a long time before Melanie Ackworth told him. The scouts had warned him that he was going to have to give up his Rover Scout badge because of his mother's conduct.'

'Losing his girl must have been the final straw,' said the inspector. 'What does he say in the formal confession?'

Christopher Enderly had just finished confessing to the premeditated murder of his mother, and the sergeant had brought the typed and signed statement in to show the inspector, who had been tied up with other matters and unable to be present.

The sergeant handed it to him silently. It was not very long. Christopher Enderly did not go into details and he did not express repentance for his act. His only regret, he said, was that he had not murdered his mother over two years earlier, when he had first found out what she was doing.

He had been studying for his accounting examination at the time and was still working with his books when his mother came home from the waitress job which she had taken the preceding year.

As the house was big and their bedrooms were in

different wings, he had heard nothing other than the sound of the front door opening and closing and muffled footsteps in the hall.

Half an hour or so later, however, he had become thirsty. Going to the kitchen for a drink, he had heard moans from the wing where his mother's bedroom was located.

Fearing that she was sick, he had gone to her door and opened it a crack with the intention of asking her if there was anything he could do.

There was no light in the room, but there was a full moon shining through the window and, to his amazement, he saw that his mother was stark naked and engaged in wildly enthusiastic sexual intercourse with an equally naked strange man.

The couple had been far too occupied to notice him and he had quietly closed the door and gone to his room, where he had had a sort of nervous breakdown.

A great many things that had puzzled him had suddenly become crystal clear. The cryptic remarks which made everyone snigger except him. The strangely sympathetic manner of some people and the way in which he had been avoided by others. The talk which had abruptly died away when he joined some group.

Everyone in Christchurch knew what his mother was doing. Like the deceived husband, he had been the last to know.

He had not known what to do. Leave Christchurch? It was as if he were letting himself be driven out of the city for something that was not his fault.

Talk to his mother? Plead with her to abandon her promiscuous affairs?

He had not been able to do that, and to the moment of her death, Sarah Enderly probably never realized that her son knew of her incredibly sordid love life.

According to Christopher, she had not known that it was her son who killed her either. He had run silently up behind her and struck a single violent blow with the hammer. She had dropped instantly, either unconscious or dead, and he had dragged her into the neglected garden and struck again and again to ensure that the deed was complete.

Ironically, it was one of the few nights that Sarah came home alone that led to her death. Had she been accompanied, her son could not have struck her down in the presence of a witness.

There was much sympathy for Christopher with the general public, and the court will, undoubtedly, grant him extreme extenuating circumstances, but whether this will save him from a life sentence for the premeditated and unrepenting murder of his mother remains a question.

9

TREASURES IN TRASH

Time meant nothing. Time had meaning only if it were possible to measure its passage.

Here there were no clocks, no day, no night, only the endlessly burning bare electric bulb suspended from the ceiling.

Still, it must be October outside. It could not possibly be more than two weeks that she had been lying here in this dirty, dry, dusty room crowded with an incredible profusion of strange objects which she could not see clearly because her glasses had been taken away. Without them, she was nearly blind.

Blind, mute and helpless. Her jaws ached and the corners of her mouth were raw from the twisted rag with which she was gagged. It was little short of ecstasy when it was removed for her feeding.

She had to be fed. Her hands were never released, nor was the garrotte which circled her throat and led down to her ankles. It was not quite long enough for her to stretch her tall, blonde, once healthy body full-length, and she often had terrible cramps in her calves and thighs.

She could not decide which was worse, the careful, gentle feeding with a spoon as if she were a small child, or the hours when he lay beside her on the heap of musty cushions, gazing steadily and expressionlessly at her sex.

He did not touch her, did not touch himself. He only looked.

For what seemed hours on end.

The fear of rape which had flooded over her when he first drew down her violet training pants and panties had long since subsided. He had forced her with the garrotte to open her legs and she had not resisted, hoping that, once he had relieved himself, he would release her.

But it had not been that simple. The man was no rapist. He was something worse, far, far worse: a complete and utter madman. He would keep her here until she died of sheer longing to be free or until the electrical wire bonds cutting into her wrists produced a fatal infection.

The door was opening. It must be feeding time again. She could see the blurred figure approaching, the hands reaching out. In a moment, he would remove the gag. The joyous anticipation of being able to close her mouth filled her.

Hands fumbled about her face, seemed to caress her cheeks, slipped beneath her chin and, suddenly, the thumbs were pressing deep into her throat!

Air! Air! She could not breathe!

There was an unbearable sensation of suffocation. Panic poured adrenaline into her bloodstream and her feet drummed in reflex agony on floor.

Not for long. With a feeling of near relief that it was, at last, all over, darkness fell upon her blood-starved brain.

A pretty, twenty-five-year-old American student was responsible for this death. She would have been horrified had she known it, for Marguerite Herries Edwards was her best friend.

And because she was, Doris Gibbs had become anxious when the twenty-four-year-old law student suddenly and inexplicably disappeared.

Doris had gone to check her room, but she had apparently not been home for several days and none of the other students could recall seeing her.

It was, of course, possible that she had gone off on a trip somewhere. It was only 10 October and the 1982 winter semester at Montpellier University in the South of France had not yet begun.

But Doris did not think so. Marguerite, she knew, had had very little money. She had failed several of her examinations recently and her scholarship was in danger. Rather than going off on trips, she had been trying to scratch up some translation work to fill out her budget.

Marguerite had had an advantage over her fellow American students in that she came from cajun country in Louisiana and had spoken and read French fluently before coming to Montpellier University in 1980.

The ability had endeared her to her fellow students, who were often in need of help with the language, but, even had she spoken no French at all, she would have been popular for she was a warm, good-natured girl and, although not beautiful, physically attractive.

Doris had finally gone to the Montpellier police, who were polite and sympathetic. Doris was lovely and they found her American accent charming.

Unfortunately, there was nothing they could do. Marguerite was an adult, and an adult could only be reported missing by a member of the family.

Doris would not be put off. The last time she had seen Marguerite was on 7 October and she had been unable to find anyone who had seen her since.

Investing a little money in a transatlantic telephone call, she informed Marguerite's father in Louisiana of the situation.

He had been as alarmed as Doris. After all, Marguerite was only studying in France because of the frightening experience she had had with her former fiancé in Louisiana. He had suddenly lost control of himself one summer evening in 1978 while they were making love and had begun to strangle her.

Marguerite had managed to break free, but the engagement was, of course, terminated and the experience had been traumatic.

In seeking a complete change of environment, France

was a natural choice because of the language and, as she was an above-average student, it had not been difficult to obtain a scholarship.

The move had not been entirely successful. In the more relaxed atmosphere of a European university, her social activities had increased and her studies had suffered accordingly.

The year before, she had encountered a twenty-nine-year-old Iranian student in his last year of medicine and they had fallen in love. He had now completed his studies and was in Los Angeles trying to obtain permission to practise there. If he succeeded, they were planning to marry – which would have terminated Marguerite's studies and was, perhaps, a reason why she was no longer so interested in them.

Doris knew these things because she was Marguerite's best friend, and she told them all to the Montpellier police when the missing-person report had been formally filed by Marguerite's father.

It did not help. All that the police were able to determine was that the very last person to have seen Marguerite was, apparently, Doris herself, and that had been on the afternoon of 7 October at a little after three o'clock.

She had seen her only at a distance and they had not spoken, but they had both waved and Doris was certain that it had been Marguerite, wearing her violet training suit as if she had just come from jogging.

No progress had been made in locating the missing girl and it was no longer possible to exclude a criminal act, so the police printed and distributed an information-wanted circular bearing Marguerite's photograph.

It would later prove to have been Marguerite's death warrant.

The circular was posted on the university bulletin board at ten in the morning of 15 October and by that evening, the strangling hands had closed Marguerite's throat forever.

120

Marguerite would not remain missing much longer. Alive, she had served a strange, incomprehensible need. Dead, she was worthless trash.

As 17 October was a Sunday, forty-four-year-old Maurice Delacourt set off in the afternoon for his weekly walk. A pleasantly egg-shaped man, larger in the middle than at either end, he was attached to the gentle pleasures of the table and, being in comfortable financial circumstances, had a slight tendency to put on weight. The Sunday walks were intended to combat this tendency and perhaps they did.

At a little after four o'clock, Maurice found Marguerite.

She was lying amidst the low dry clumps of heather and broom covering a rise in the land known as the Mottes Redounes near the hamlet of Matelles, a good five miles from Montpellier.

Marguerite's bonds and gag had been removed, but she was still wearing her violet training suit, now very dirty, as she had worn it ever since her disappearance – with the pants and underpants pulled down so that her body was exposed from the navel to the knees.

Maurice Delacourt logically assumed that she had been raped and murdered, no uncommon occurrence in a civilized country such as France. Having tried in vain to detect any sign of life, he made off, as fast as his weight and physical condition would permit, to raise the alarm.

A police patrol car arrived quickly. The apparent fact of homicide was confirmed, although there was no identification of the victim as yet, and the Montpellier Gendarmerie was alerted.

At five o'clock, Inspector Jerome Orsini, Detective Sergeant Pierre-Louis Massenet and Dr Charles Sablon, all members of the gendarmerie department of criminal investigations, arrived at the scene.

While the inspector and the sergeant looked over the surrounding area, the doctor, a dark-haired, olive-skinned man with a neatly trimmed black moustache, began his examination of the body.

It did not take him very long. The woman, he said, had been dead for at least two days. The cause of death was manual strangulation. She did not appear to have been raped. And there were multiple marks and abrasions on the body which he was anxious to examine in the morgue. He therefore recommended that the body be taken there as quickly as possible.

The inspector was in agreement. There were no indications that the murder had been committed at this place and the body had presumably been brought there simply for disposal. There would be no clues to recover and there was no reason to hold the body until the technicians from the gendarmerie laboratory had concluded their investigations at the scene.

The body of Marguerite Herries Edwards, still anonymous, was, therefore, removed to the gendarmerie morgue in Montpellier, where it did not remain anonymous long.

The official identification was made by a sorrowfully weeping Doris Gibbs and other friends of the dead girl. They saw only the face as the body had already been opened for the autopsy.

The autopsy resulted in a highly interesting report. Dr Sablon was able to determine that the victim had been bound with something thin and smooth for nearly a week, had worn a garrotte around the neck, had been gagged continually, had slept on something hard, dusty and dirty, had been unable to wash herself or even clean herself following urination and bowel movement which, he suggested, had taken place in a rusty bucket as the mark of the rim was still present on her buttocks and the backs of her thighs.

She had not been molested sexually. There had been no penetration of the genitals and there were no traces of either semen or saliva in or on the body. The exposed condition in which she had been found, he suggested, had been a clumsy attempt to simulate a sex crime.

Cause of death had been manual strangulation by someone with rather small hands, and the time of death was the afternoon of 15 October between five-thirty and seven-thirty. She had made no attempt to defend herself, presumably because she was bound at the time.

'A remarkably mysterious case,' said Inspector Orsini. 'The girl must have been held prisoner somewhere from October seventh until the fifteenth, when she was killed because the wanted circulars panicked her captor.'

A short, squat man, broad in the chest and broad in the forehead, he had just finished reading the autopsy report and handed it to Sergeant Massenet.

The sergeant, equally short, equally broad, but twenty years younger, made a sort of grunting noise of assent.

'In a way, we killed her by looking for her,' he said. 'What do you think it was, a mental case?'

'Possibly,' said the inspector. 'There was no sexual motive and it certainly wasn't a question of ransom. About the only other possibility would be political.'

'Political?' said the sergeant. 'She was in politics?'

'Of course not,' said the inspector impatiently. 'But her boy friend was an Iranian. The different factions of Iranians here in France have been killing each other ever since the Shah left.'

'But she wasn't Iranian,' objected the sergeant.

'God damn it, Pierre-Louis,' said the inspector. 'Her fiancé was, and he's in the US. People like that are so crazy that, if they couldn't get at him directly, they might go indirectly through her. In any case, that's what we're going to start with. Check with the alien registration office and see how many Iranians there are here, and we'll see what we can do about turning up a potential suspect.'

'I think I'll start by finding out what kind of an Iranian the boy friend is, pro-Khomeini or anti,' said the sergeant thoughtfully. 'That should eliminate half the suspects immediately.'

It was actually rather less than half of the suspects who were eliminated. Marguerite's fiancé turned out to be an anti-Khomeini Iranian and they were in a minority among the university students, which was what nearly all of the Iranians in Montpellier were.

'In my opinion, any of them would have been capable of it and worse,' said the sergeant, reporting on the Iranian lead to the inspector, 'but I doubt that any of them did because none of them have the facilities for holding a woman prisoner. They're practically all living in single furnished rooms and their landladies keep a sharp eye on them.'

'All right,' said the inspector, 'but keep a couple of men on the terrorist angle. It's in style now. Maybe some young terrorist trying to make a name for himself killed her because she was an American capitalist. We've had crazier motives.'

The sergeant assigned a team to continue investigating the possibilities of a political motive, although he privately thought it improbable, and altered the main thrust of the investigation to an intense survey of such social contacts as Marguerite had made during her stay in France.

It was almost certain that the murderer was someone resident in Montpellier or the surrounding communities. Who else would have had the facilities for holding a girl prisoner for over a week?

The inspector and the sergeant had both thought for a time that it might be Marguerite's former fiancé. They had learned of the strangling incident in Louisiana from Doris Gibbs and had seen a possible significance in the fact that Marguerite had died of strangulation in Montpellier.

The fiancé had had no known motive for the attempted murder and there was no known motive for the murder. If he had been insane enough to strangle her in Louisiana, he might be insane enough to follow her to France and finish the job.

Although the reasoning was flawless, the theory had come to nothing as an inquiry to the American police produced the information that the fiancé was in Louisiana and had not left there at any time during October.

There was no more success with the investigation into Marguerite's contacts. It failed to produce any plausible or even possible suspect. Nearly all of her friends had been students or university personnel and none of them were in a position to hold a woman prisoner, even if they had been strange enough to want to.

The investigators were running out of possibilities, but, fortunately, they were not alone.

Doris Gibbs was still running up and down, determined to do whatever she could to bring the murderer of her friend to justice, and on 5 November, she made an important discovery.

It was Marguerite's bicycle, a near-antique English model and the sole example of its kind in Montpellier, and it was leaning against the wall outside the Faculty of Science laboratory.

Doris did not touch it. She immediately notified Sergeant Massenet, who hurried to the scene and found the bicycle secured with a chain and padlock, the normal precaution taken by people who did not want their bicycles stolen.

He did not touch it either, but summoned the technicians from the laboratory and the identification section. They examined the bicycle and reported that it was covered with Marguerite's fingerprints, but no one else's, and had been standing against the wall for close to a month or, in short, from the presumed date of Marguerite's disappearance.

The conclusion which the inspector and the sergeant drew from this was that Marguerite had disappeared somewhere in the university itself, and they now recalled

125

that the last known sighting of the girl had been at the university by Doris Gibbs.

Doris did not need to be summoned to testify. She was already waiting outside the inspector's office.

She too recalled that it had been at the university and outside the laboratory building of the Faculty of Science that she had last seen Marguerite, and she recalled something else.

Marguerite had not been alone. She had been standing and speaking to one of the university maintenance technicians, a small, largely bald man with a bad limp who was popular among the students as he liked to talk and was handy at fixing things. His name was Leon Deshayes.

And Doris remembered still more. On 15 October, the day that Marguerite had been murdered, she had run into Deshayes, who had asked her if she had seen Marguerite. He had, he said, found some translation work for her.

Doris had thought it strange that he did not know Marguerite was missing. Normally, he knew everything that was going on at the university, and Marguerite's friends had been searching for her for several days already.

'Well, he's a better suspect than no suspect at all,' said the inspector doubtfully, after Doris had left. 'But check him out. Maybe he owns a villa where he keeps girls prisoner.'

'One room would do, if it was private,' said the sergeant. 'I think he's our man.'

And because he thought so, he assigned a squad of his best men to investigate Deshayes' background and circumstances, which turned out to be more remarkable than even the sergeant had expected them to be.

Unfortunately, the circumstances were not such as to make Deshayes a better suspect. Quite the contrary. Given his situation, it was difficult to see how he could

126

have found the privacy to murder anybody, let alone hold a large young woman prisoner for days on end.

'This Deshayes,' said the sergeant, making an interim report on the investigation, 'is one of the great weirdos of all time, but, compared to his wife, he's super-normal. You want to hear it from the beginning?'

The inspector did.

'Deshayes is fifty-three years old,' said the sergeant. 'He was originally an unskilled labourer, but in 1958 he had an on-the-job accident which left him lame. He was, consequently, given a training of sorts and placed with the university as a maintenance technician, which means janitor. He cleans things, scrubs the floors and so on. Salary is six thousand francs a month.'

'Not bad,' said the inspector. 'So what's weird about that?'

'Wait,' said the sergeant. 'On 11 January 1962, he married a school teacher named Andrea Picard, three years younger than himself. She was and still is completely bonkers and she turned Deshayes bonkers too.'

'Not the first such mental casualty to marriage,' said the inspector, 'but go on.'

'Mrs Deshayes was active in collecting old clothes and other junk for the benefit of Third World charity organizations while she was still a teacher,' said the sergeant. 'Whether because of this or coincidentally, she became depressive, mixed up and obsessed with collecting junk of any kind. The only thing was, she didn't pass it on to the Third World. She kept it herself.'

'Where?' said the inspector curiously.

'Wait,' said the sergeant. 'After a time, Mrs Deshayes became too nutty even to be a teacher and she was given early retirement. Pension: four thousand francs a month.'

'That's ten thousand a month between them,' observed the inspector. 'They could afford a villa.'

'They own,' said the sergeant, reading from a list, 'five

apartments, of which one is in the new luxury residence Palavas des Flots. In addition, they rent two other apartments and two cellars. They own two Renault R16s, a Renault R20TS and a Volkswagen bus. Guess where they sleep.'

'In the Salvation Army shelter?' said the inspector.

'In the Renault R20,' said the sergeant. 'You know why?'

'They're motor sport fans,' said the inspector.

'Because the seven apartments, the two cellars, the two R16s and the Volkswagen bus are full to the rafters with trash and garbage,' said the sergeant. 'That's all they do when he's not working, sift through dustbins and carry off the things that take their fancy. Everything takes their fancy. One more couple like that and Montpellier would be the only city in France not to have a rubbish disposal problem.'

'But a health one,' said the inspector, 'or do they take only dry trash, not real garbage?'

'Garbage too,' said the sergeant. 'It's what they eat. He collects the left-overs off the plates in the university restaurant and she digs around behind the greengrocer's shops and markets for discarded vegetables and fruit.'

'Good,' said the inspector. 'You've convinced me. Deshayes and his wife are as crazy as cockroaches in a cocaine factory. Why does this make them suspects in the Edwards murder? They couldn't have kept her prisoner in one of their apartments if they can't even get in to sleep there themselves.'

'Edwards was killed by a crazy person,' said the sergeant, ticking off the points on his fingers, 'because there was no motive. She was last seen talking to Deshayes. Her bicycle was found outside the Faculty of Science laboratory, which is one of the buildings Deshayes cleans and has keys to. There were very few people around the university at that time because the courses hadn't started then. The laboratory has samples of the dirt from the room she was kept in. I think they'll match one of the unused store rooms or basements in the university.'

'And, by God, I think so too,' said the inspector.

They were both right. Locating the room in which Marguerite had been held prisoner was not difficult. All that was required was to determine from the maintenance department of the university what keys were in Deshayes possession. Only two were to store rooms that were seldom visited and the investigators hit on it first.

Although the laboratory would later match samples of the dirt from the floor of the room with samples taken from Marguerite's body and clothing, it was not really necessary. The discarded bonds and gag were lying there, stained with her blood. The rusty bucket provided as a toilet had not been emptied. The pile of musty cushions still lay near where marks in the dust on the floor indicated the outline of a human body. And, perhaps most poignant souvenir of all, Marguerite's glasses lay on a shelf, together with the retorts, test tubes and other pieces of equipment for which the laboratory no longer had use.

Arrested and charged with sequestration and homicide. Leon Deshayes denied all knowledge of the crime and claimed that he had not seen Marguerite since the end of August, when she had asked him to help her find some translation work.

Doris Gibbs, however, swore that she had seen Deshayes with Marguerite on 7 October and, when he was taken to the store room and confronted with the evidence of his crime, he broke down and confessed.

It was true that Marguerite had asked him to help her find translation work in the university and he had made an appointment for her to come and talk the matter over at three-thirty in the afternoon of 7 October.

Marguerite had come and they had talked while he was cleaning the laboratory. He admitted that he had already been planning to take her prisoner at this time, but she had suspected nothing and, as it was getting on for dinner time, had accepted his offer to fetch some food from the university restaurant, Le Boutonnet.

By the time they had eaten, it was already quite late and he had told her that the university gates were closed and that she would not be able to get out until morning.

She had been alarmed, but he had calmed her, saying that he knew of a place in the building where she could sleep.

She had followed him unsuspectingly to the store room and, as she passed through the door, he had snatched off her glasses and pushed her to the floor.

Marguerite had screamed and fought, but there were only maintenance personnel at the university and they had gone home. Handicapped by the loss of her glasses, she had been overpowered, and Deshayes had tied her hands with electrical wire and gagged her.

The description of what he had done was logical and intelligible. What was not were his reasons for it. Despite all his best efforts, he could think of none.

He had had no illusions about raping Marguerite. He had been sexually impotent for over five years at the time. He had also had no illusions about the possibility of ever releasing his captive. Had it not been for the wanted circular which had frightened him, he would have kept Marguerite prisoner for as long as she lived.

Leon Deshayes' confession was made on 26 January 1983 after forty hours of interrogation, and it will be a long time before the psychologists and psychiatrists can decide whether he is sane enough to be held responsible for his actions.

His wife was completely exonerated of all guilt or knowledge of the crime and took the matter calmly.

'I have to get busy now and round up a lot of bottles for the deposits,' she said. 'So that we can pay for Leon's legal expenses.'

130

10

INTERESTING NEIGHBOURS

'Bones in the breasts?' said Peter Gross. 'I don't believe
it. The breastbone, sure, but . . .'

'Those aren't bones,' said Karin Peters, his plump but
athletic companion. 'They're plastic breast implants. A
friend of mine just last year . . .'

'Well, whatever they are, this is a human skeleton,'
interrupted Peter, 'and we have to report it immediately.
Where do you think the nearest telephone would be?'

Tall, thin and not very athletic, Peter was not familiar
with the low, wooded mountains of the Eifel, a region
to the west of the Rhine in West Germany.

A native of Hamburg, he had come down to the city
of Duesseldorf, thirty miles to the north of where he was
now standing, to work in an advertising agency.

Karin had been working in the same agency and their
relationship had quickly progressed beyond the purely
professional. On this Wednesday, 18 July 1979, they
were embarking on their first camping trip together and
had arrived in the Eifel only that morning.

It was now nearly noon and, after hiking for what
seemed to Peter several hundred miles, they had begun
looking for a place to set up their small tent.

He had just started across a tiny meadow in the open
mixed forest of beeches and conifers when something
under his boots went crack.

Intrigued, he had given the ground a kick and
uncovered the top of a skull.

Never having had anything to do with skulls before,

he had not immediately realized what it was and continued to kick the earth and sod away until it became clear that here lay the remains of a human being.

Or was it? The skull was equipped with not only one, but two jaw-bones, and one of them was filled with a startling array of long, sharp teeth!

Even though the skeleton was only partly uncovered, it was obvious that there were too many and the wrong kind of bones, and lying among them were two hairy, leathery, sharp-pointed ears.

The round white disks which Peter had taken for breast bones, but which Karin had recognized as plastic breast implants, lay on top of the rib-cage on either side.

Although it was not far from the point where the skeleton was buried to Lake Rur, where there was a campsite and several hotels, they did not know this, and Peter trotted the mile and a quarter back to the village of Nideggen, which they had passed on the way out.

His companion remained behind with the skeleton. They were afraid that they would not be able to find it again otherwise.

Karin later confessed that she had become quite frightened while waiting for Peter to return with the police. She possessed a solid set of nerves and she was used to camping in the woods of the Eifel, but the idea of a monster lying buried there worked upon her imagination.

It was as if the woods had suddenly become lonely, isolated, much too quiet. Although it was a bright, sunny midsummer day, she had had the impression that it was growing dark.

When she thought that she saw the bones in the shallow grave move, she turned and walked quickly away until she could no longer see them.

Nideggen is a charming village of seven thousand three hundred permanent residents and, although it has a surprising number of hotels and taverns, it has very few policemen.

132

They are not needed. Nothing illegal ever happens in Nideggen and, if something did, it would be taken care of by the police in Dueren, a larger community ten miles to the north.

The main contribution of the constable who returned with Peter was, therefore, a precise knowledge of the district, which enabled him to reach the scene with a police car by making use of the forestry logging trails.

Having taken an unbelieving look at the skeleton, he left Peter with Karin, to her considerable relief, and drove to Lake Rur, where he telephoned a confirmation of Peter's report to the station in Nideggen.

There was, he said, the skeleton of a strange monster lying in the forest approximately a quarter of a mile to the north-east of Lake Rur. It looked to him like the remains of a circus freak.

'Nonsense,' said Dr Ulrich Bauer, squatting down to poke among the bones, which had now been laid bare. 'It's a perfectly normal female skeleton and she's been buried with her dog under her head. A little disarrangement, probably by small animals. Hard to say how long she's been here. A few years, at least. I'll be able to obtain a more exact date when I get her into the laboratory.'

The laboratory was in Wiesbaden, close to a hundred miles to the south-east, and the doctor had been summoned by the Dueren police because he was one of the country's leading experts on human bones.

A stocky, irritable man with glasses and a salt-and-pepper beard, he was kept travelling almost continuously. An astonishing number of human skeletons turn up in Germany, considering that it is a small country, and, while some date from the Second World War, others are more recent.

The Dueren department of criminal investigations had called in the doctor when their efforts to identify the victim failed. She apparently had been buried stark naked.

Unlike Peter and Karin and the Nideggen constable, they had not taken the bones for those of a monster. But they had not known exactly what they were either, and the Dueren coroner had declared any further investigation beyond his competence.

Such investigations were Dr Bauer's speciality and, having completed his examination of the bones at the scene, he had them transferred to Wiesbaden, where he arrived at an impressive number of conclusions with regard to the person of whom they had once formed a part.

She had, he said, been a woman in her mid-thirties, five feet two inches tall and weighing a hundred and ten pounds. She had died about two years previously of strangulation, suffocation, drowning, loss of blood or natural causes. The second finger of her left hand had been broken shortly before or at the time of her death.

She had never had a broken bone previously, but there was considerable dental work and she had had plastic implants in both breasts to increase the size and improve the shape. As such surgery was not cheap, it was possible that she had belonged to one of the performing arts where the size and shape of the breasts were professionally important.

The dog buried with her was a wire-haired terrier. It had died on the same date as the woman as the result of a smashed skull, the implement used having been, perhaps, an ordinary carpenter's hammer.

Diagrams and photographs of the dental work and the breast implants were included with Dr Bauer's report and copies were sent to police units throughout Germany and, because Nideggen is less than ten miles from the border, Belgium.

Normally, it would have been the dental work which provided the identification, but, in this case, it proved to be the breast implants.

A doctor in Duesseldorf who specialized in cosmetic surgery recognized them as a special pair which he had implanted in a thirty-four-year-old photographic model called Magdalena Blum eight years earlier, when gravity had begun to exercise an unfortunate effect on her professional equipment.

Armed with the knowledge of her name and profession, the police soon located Miss Blum's dentist, who completed the identification by confirming that the dental work was his.

As Magdalena Blum had been a free-lance model and not employed by any one studio, she had not been reported missing by the people with whom she worked, but had only been roundly cursed when she failed to show up for her appointments.

She had, however, been reported missing by her mother, but only after she had been dead for more than a month. As she had been resident in the town of Neuss am Rhein at the time, the missing-person report had been filed there, and it was now the Neuss department of criminal investigations which took over the case.

There was no certainty that Magdalena Blum had been murdered in Neuss or even murdered at all, but the crushed skull of the dog was an indication of violence and the burial in the forest without identification constituted sufficient reason to suspect a criminal act. Therefore, the case was immediately classed as homicide.

Miss Blum's next of kin, her mother, confirmed that her daughter had owned a wire-haired terrier named Schnuppi. It was partly because Schnuppi had disappeared at the same time that she had not reported her missing earlier. She had thought that, if Magdalena had taken the dog with her, it meant that she had gone off voluntarily.

Mrs Blum did not live in Neuss herself and, although she was on good terms with her daughter, she did not see her very often.

Magdalena, she said, had worried about her age and

had been anxious to marry and give up her career. However, despite her oustandingly good looks, she had not seemed able to find the right man for a husband.

A number of candidates had not worked out, but her mother did not know whether she had had anyone at the time of her death and, if so, who he was.

At the time of the disappearance, she had thought that Magdalena had finally found someone suitable and had impulsively gone off with him on what passed for a honeymoon in modern society.

Magdalena's landlord had called at the middle of June to say that the rent had not been paid and he had been unable to contact Magdalena. He knew her mother's address because she had signed the lease as a guarantor, and he expected her to make up the rent.

Mrs Blum had come down to Neuss. Neither she nor the landlord had a key to the apartment, which was on the third floor of a new building at 12 Schiller Strasse, so she summoned the police and a locksmith to open the door. As it was not her apartment, the police had to be present.

Somewhat to her relief, she found that Magdalena's personal identity papers, her toilet articles and some of her clothing were missing. So was Schnuppi, and Mrs Blum came to the conclusion that her daughter had simply gone off and stuck her with the unpaid rent.

It was because she was annoyed with Magdalena for going off like that without saying anything that she had reported her missing, rather than because she thought something had happened to her.

For the police, it had been an unfortunate conclusion. More than two years had now elapsed, making it extremely difficult to trace Magdalena Blum's romantic interests at the time of her death.

There were, however, hardly any other conceivable suspects with a plausible motive. Magdalena had been a successful model, but she had not been rich and, even if she had been killed in the course of an attempted robbery, the robber would scarcely have gone to the trouble of carrying her body out to the woods thirty miles away and burying it with her dog.

The only possible explanation for this careful disposal of the corpse was that there was a connection between Magdalena and her murderer which could be traced and, as it was not professional, it could only be personal.

'As for the dog,' said Inspector Walter Metzler, the short, balding chief of the Neuss homicide squad, speaking around the thick stump of his cigar, 'it probably died trying to defend its mistress.'

'Probably,' agreed his assistant, a dedicated-looking, young detective sergeant with blond side whiskers and round blue eyes whose name was Maximilian Friedmann. 'Could be too that he was afraid to leave it in her apartment because it would bark and call attention to her disappearance. Couldn't have taken it with him. It would have been a dead give-away.'

'What makes you think it happened in her apartment?' asked the inspector curiously.

'Where else?' said the sergeant. 'It wasn't there in the woods.'

'You're right for the wrong reason,' said the inspector. 'The reason that it presumably happened in her apartment is that her papers and clothes were missing and the murderer probably took them, though God knows why.'

'Probably,' agreed the sergeant. 'Of course, he could have taken her keys to let himself in after he murdered her. Could be that he was looking for something in the apartment and didn't find it – or maybe he did, after all, because her papers are missing, aren't they?'

'Humph-mumph,' grunted the inspector, chewing on the cigar. He sometimes felt that his assistant thought of rather too many possibilities. 'The actual scene of the crime doesn't matter much now anyway. After this length of time there probably isn't much hope of finding anything useful.'

'Probably not,' assented the sergeant. 'The lab chief says they can recover hair and textile fragments as much as five years old.'

'But not when there have been other people living in the apartment for the past two years,' said the inspector, becoming a little impatient.

'Probably not . . .' began the sergeant and, catching his chief's eye, came to a halt.

There was a short silence in the office.

'That's better,' grunted the inspector with some satisfaction, and returned to the file he had been studying.

The sergeant was young and dedicated, but the inspector was experienced and it was, therefore, the inspector who was right. There was little hope of solving a murder two years old of which none of the circumstances were known, including whether it was a murder or not.

A painstaking investigation of the persons with whom Magdalena had associated at the time was carried out, but the results were largely negative. Many were found who could not have murdered Magdalena. None were found who had had any reason to.

Worse yet, the investigators could not be certain that they had identified all of Magdalena's contacts. Significantly, perhaps, they had found no evidence that she had had any close male friend in the period immediately preceding her disappearance.

The situation was, however, not as hopeless as it seemed. Another and larger police department was also working on the Magdalena Blum case, although the Neuss investigators did not know it.

Nor, for that matter, did the other police department's investigators know it either.

What the Duesseldorf police were officially investigating was not homicide, but a modern version of the old badger game in which a husband and wife team attempt to lure a well-to-do victim into a sexually compromising situation and milk him dry.

At one time, a lucrative field for enterprising men with attractive young wives, the sex revolution had nearly ruined the business.

Respectable businessmen who would once have been terrified by the threat of exposure of sexual dalliance with a married lady the age of their granddaughter were now more inclined to boast. Compromising photographs were no longer purchased at fabulous prices, but were copied and shown to the victim's friends and, if the sexual liberation was very thorough, his wife.

As runaway inflation ruins pickpockets, the media's sex revolution had ruined the practitioners of the badger game.

The human mind is, however, ingenious and inventive, particularly where money is concerned, and new forms of the profession had arisen.

Generally, they involved violence. If the victim did not mind being exposed as a lecher, he often had deep-seated objections to having his genitals kicked off by a supposedly outraged husband. As the socialist-dominated courts had come to the conclusion that there was no such thing as a bad, young and poor person, the young and poor had little to fear for wreaking their just rage on the more wealthy members of an unfair society.

Thus reasoned thirty-two-year-old Peter Okrent, who, during the relatively short intervals when he was establishing a fresh claim to unemployment compensation, was an electrician, a profession which did not appeal to him as it involved work.

Unemployment compensation was not satisfactory either as there was not enough of it. Peter had an expensive hobby. He was a pornography fan and the material to which he was attracted was not cheap.

That Peter was in need of pornography at all might seem surprising for he was married to an eighteen-year-old Spanish girl named Theresa, who was very lovely, possessed of an exceedingly warm nature and troubled by few inhibitions.

Peter appreciated this, but it also eventually occurred to him that Theresa could be put to other and more lucrative uses. Investing some of his unemployment compensation in a large and dangerous-looking pistol, he and Theresa began to comb the better-class bars in search of a mark.

They soon found one and inveigled him with little difficulty into a tender encounter of the dangerous kind with Theresa. Peter came bounding in with his pistol to offer a choice between payment and a painful treatment of the offending parts of the victim's anatomy.

The victim, whose intelligence level was roughly double that of both young entrepreneurs combined, promptly agreed to everything, but said that he had no cash. Would Peter accept a cheque?

Peter would and was, of course, arrested immediately when he tried to cash it.

This was on 1 July 1977 and, to Peter's indignation, he was charged not only with blackmail, but threats with a deadly weapon, possession of an unauthorized firearm and procuring.

He was to have further reason for indignation for, having been brought to trial, he was found guilty and, on 8 September 1978, sentenced to eight years' imprisonment.

Theresa had supported Peter in all his work, but she appeared to be sincerely doubtful as to whether what they had done was ethical. She was also very young and pretty and the jury was all male.

Even so, there had been such a change of heart in the judiciary that Theresa was given three and a half years and the sentences were not even suspended.

The officers of the Duesseldorf department of criminal investigations were, therefore, well pleased with the results of their labours and considered the case closed.

And so it would have been had Peter Okrent not

sought to bring about a reduction in the length of his sentence. Aware that there were many programmes available for making useful members of society out of convicted felons, he saw no reason why he should not take advantage of one of them to gain his freedom.

Actually, there was a very good reason why he would have been better off to leave sleeping dogs lie.

It did not, however, occur to him and, as a result, a junior detective attached to the Duesseldorf department of criminal investigations was instructed to dig out Okrent's file so that a parole board could search through it for excuses to release him.

And, very unfortunately for Peter Okrent, this junior detective happened to have an excellent memory, so that when he read Okrent's address in Neuss am Rhein, which was where he and Theresa had been living at the time of their arrest, he was struck with the certainty that he had seen this address somewhere before.

It could not have been in connection with Okrent's case, however, for he had not worked on it and had actually never heard of it until being sent to dig out the file.

Finally, after racking his brains for over an hour, he came to the conclusion that he had seen the address in one of the information-requested circulars which were sent round to all police units in the area from time to time.

These were on file and, hunting back through the circulars, he soon came upon one from the Neuss department of criminal investigations. It concerned the unsolved maybe-homicide of Magdalena Blum.

The detective, who knew the fearful consequences of not going through channels, did not contact Neuss. Instead, he brought the matter to the attention of his immediate superior, who turned it over to the Duesseldorf homicide squad. They informed Inspector Metzler in Neuss that they had a potential suspect in his murder case in jail.

Inspector Metzler and Sergeant Friedberg both came immediately to Duesseldorf. There was no evidence that Peter Okrent had had anything to do with whatever had befallen Magdalena Blum, but he had been her next-door neighbour at the time of her disappearance, he was a convicted felon and, above all, he was the only potential suspect in the case ever to have turned up.

The inspector and the sergeant did not, however, see Okrent immediately. Having spoken with the officers who had handled the Duesseldorf case, it was obvious that interrogating him would merely have the effect of putting him on his guard.

Peter Okrent was not a man to lose his head and make self-incriminating admissions, nor was he likely to be overcome by qualms of conscience.

This made the inspector unhappy for, the more that he studied Okrent's file, the more he became convinced that he was a very good suspect indeed.

The sergeant did not think so. 'He doesn't have any previous criminal record,' he argued. 'The man has a profession. He's married. Head of a family. Probably had a tough time making ends meet. His wife was probably hounding him for things he couldn't afford to give her. The whole thing was probably her idea.'

'Then I suppose you would say that *she* probably murdered Magdalena Blum?' said the inspector, cocking a sardonic eye in the direction of his assistant and shifting the cigar to the other corner of his mouth.

'Probably,' acquiesced the sergeant automatically, 'but . . . I didn't say that! Why should she anyway?'

The inspector shrugged. 'Jealousy,' he said. 'Okrent has the morals of a mink in a marijuana patch. Blum was beautiful, a model, lived right next door. She was hard-up, wanted to get married. They were making it and Theresa caught them. Hot-headed. Spanish blood, you know . . .'

The sergeant was becoming bewildered. 'But Mrs

Okrent is a small woman,' he said. 'Blum wasn't big, but she was solid. I don't see how . . .?'

'You don't know the southerners,' said the inspector. 'She probably strangled her with her bare hands and . . .'

Probably concurred the sergeant without really knowing what he was saying. 'But she couldn't have carried her all the way . . .'

'Damn it! You're right!' said the inspector in mock fury. 'That kills the theory. He'd have had to help get rid of the body and we know he wouldn't do something illegal like that, don't we?'

'You didn't mean any of it,' said the sergeant reproachfully.

'I didn't when I started,' said the inspector, 'but I'm beginning to wonder now.'

'Whether Mrs Okrent actually did it?' said the sergeant.

'No,' said the inspector. 'Whether we could persuade her to tell us who did.'

What had occurred to Inspector Metzler while taking the mickey out of his assistant was that, in the police and court records which he had just been reading, Theresa Okrent had appeared to be sincerely repentant.

If the repentance was real and not simply feigned in order to influence the court, she might want to clear her conscience by confessing to whatever she knew about the murder of Magdalena Blum.

The inspector thought it over for the rest of the day, discussed the matter with Sergeant Friedmann and asked the opinion of the investigations officers who had handled Okrent's badger-game case.

In the end, all were in agreement, even the sergeant. There was no other lead to follow, no other potential suspect. It was Theresa Okrent or no one. The inspector had nothing to lose.

Theresa Okrent was brought to police headquarters in Neuss, where Inspector Metzler carried out the interrogation personally. He could be very persuasive when necessary, but, as it turned out, no great powers of persuasion were needed. Theresa Okrent's repentance was sincere indeed. She talked, and at length.

When she finished talking, she had achieved something unusual for a woman of her age: she had shocked a seasoned criminal investigations officer.

The murder, said Theresa, had taken place on the evening of Wednesday, 1 June 1977.

She and Peter had been sitting in the living room of their apartment. He had been thumbing through his collection of pornographic magazines in search of a little stimulus. Theresa, who needed none, was waiting patiently for what would happen once Peter had been stimulated.

It was the way they spent most of their evenings, she said, but this evening had been different. Suddenly laying down his magazine, Peter said, 'Why don't we ask the neighbour over for a drink? It would be friendly and the sex would be more fun with three of us.'

Theresa found nothing strange in this suggestion and went over to knock on Magdalena Blum's door. Neither she nor Peter knew her other than to speak to in the hall.

Magdalena unsuspectingly accepted the offer of a drink. There was no reason for her to be suspicious. The Okrents were an attractive young couple and she, undoubtedly, felt there could be no danger when both husband and wife were present.

Poor, lonely Magdalena did not even receive the promised drink. Instead, no sooner had she passed through the door of the Okrent apartment than she found herself looking into the barrel of the pistol which Peter had bought as an investment in the badger game.

Theresa was ordered to put handcuffs on the guest and, being a good, obedient wife, promptly did so.

Magdalena was then stripped to the skin, gagged and

given a thorough whipping with a leather whip which Peter had bought from a sex toy mail-order house.

Following the whipping, Theresa was told to bring out her sewing box and Peter tortured the guest by thrusting needles and pins into her sex organs and breasts.

This stimulated him sufficiently. He not only raped Magdalena, but engaged in sex with his wife as well.

He then removed Magdalena's gag, and she made a fatal error.

Had she said nothing. or pretended that she had enjoyed the hospitality of her hosts, Peter might have been stupid enough to let her go. But Magdalena was hurting in a great many places and outraged beyond all measure.

The instant that the gag was removed, she made many uncomplimentary remarks concerning Peter, Theresa and Peter's mother, whom she accused of unnatural, illegal and probably impossible sexual acts in becoming pregnant with him. She ended with the assurance that she was going straight to the police and they would then see.

Under the circumstances, these were suicidal utterances and Magdalena had obviously been insane with rage and humiliation to make them.

Made they were, however, and Peter promptly took the necessary action, looping a silk scarf around her neck and pulling it tight with the intention of strangling her.

In a desperate attempt to ward off her death, Magdalena raised her handcuffed hands and managed to get her fingers under the scarf.

Peter yelled at Theresa to pull her hands away and she obeyed. It was, it seemed, this act more than anything else which bothered her and moved her to confess.

After Theresa had pulled Magdalena's hands away from the scarf, Peter continued to draw it tighter until the victim lost consciousness and eventually died.

It took, said Theresa, a long time.

The body was then carried down to the car, wrapped in a carpet, and left in the trunk until the next day. Then they drove to the Eifel and buried it, together with Magdalena's dog, Schnuppi.

Peter had remarked after they took Magdalena's corpse down to the car that they would also have to get rid of the dog or it would betray them. She did not know whether he thought the dog would be able to communicate with someone over the murder or whether he meant that he would bark when no one came to feed him. In any case, he had gone to the apartment amd killed the dog with a hammer.

The day following, after they had disposed of the bodies in the forest, they returned to Magdalena's apartment and took away all of her private papers, which they burned, and such of her possessions as they thought they could use.

Peter had never mentioned the matter again and she thought he had forgotten it. It had, however, preyed on Theresa's mind.

Considering that without her help the case would probably never have been solved, the court was not especially generous.

On 9 May 1980, she was found guilty of acting as an accessary to murder and sentenced to ten years' imprisonment.

The court was not kind to Peter Okrent either. He was sentenced to life imprisonment.

11

POOR NATALIE

The fight in front of the Cézanne cinema was more entertaining than most. In the first place, the combatants were both pretty young women and, second, neither appeared to be wearing underwear. As they rolled on the pavement, hooked hands locked in each other's hair, there was a spatter of applause from the mainly male audience.

Regrettably, the spectacle did not last long. The younger of the two women, monstrously pregnant, banged the head of her opponent against the cement with such violence that she became dazed and ceased to struggle. Leaping to her feet, the victor began kicking her helpless enemy savagely in the breasts and belly.

The pregnant girl's companion, dirty, long-haired and with a pitiful attempt at a beard, continued to watch with a dreamy, smiling expression and made no move to intervene.

Others of the onlookers, perhaps fearing a summons as a witness in a murder case, laid hands on the raging woman and dragged her off her victim.

An ambulance was called; the injured woman was lifted into it and driven away to the hospital.

A police patrol car arrived and the officers began questioning the spectators.

No one knew anything. When the girl who had carried out the assault was asked for her name and address, she replied that it was none of the police's business. Her companion did not reply at all, gazing benignly on the officers with unfocused eyes.

Eventually, two or three persons were found, all women, who said that the pregnant woman had been involved in the fight, but by this time the girl and her companion had gone.

The officers shrugged and went back to their beat. The participants had obviously all been what the French call marginals, persons living on the fringes of society, unemployed and unemployable, squatting in abandoned buildings and engaging in a little prostitution and theft to finance whatever drugs they were addicted to. The quarrel had probably been over the male companion. Both women had wanted him and had been unwilling to share.

Marginals or not, the matter was legally assault and battery and on Tuesday, 22 June 1982, a bored detective from the department of criminal investigations of the Aix-en-Provence police went around to the hospital to take a statement from the victim. The fight had taken place at approximately eight-thirty of the preceding evening and the victim would, presumably, be capable of making a statement by now.

But not, as the detective expected, willing. The woman, who was not seriously injured, identified herself, rather reluctantly, as Hélène Thomi, aged thirty-four, divorced and living on public assistance. She had never seen her assailant before in her life, she said, and she had no idea why she had attacked her. She did not want to prefer charges.

The detective took all this down without comment, although he did not believe a word of it, and returned to headquarters.

Before closing the case, he ran the name through the records section computer and was rewarded with the information that the woman had been charged on four occasions with contributing to the delinquency of minors.

Mrs Thomi's interest in adolescent boys was, it seemed, not altogether motherly. None of the cases had come to trial, for lack of evidence. The victims had suffered little injury and were unwilling to testify.

None of this was very unusual. Aix-en-Provence, a charming, gracious city of some one hundred and twenty thousand inhabitants in the South of France, is a university town, and marginals tend to congregate around universities. If you are dirty, promiscuous, idle and wear your hair long, you can always claim to be a student.

Or an artist. Or a writer.

The detective, therefore, closed the file with the remark that this was some sort of squabble among members of the marginal society and that, as no charges had been preferred, no further action needed to be taken. It then being nearly five-thirty in the afternoon, he had a beer in the police canteen and went home.

As might be expected for the place and time of year, the weather was clear, sunny and becoming remarkably warm. The summer solstice was two days away and it would get dark only by nine o'clock.

Three hours later, almost twenty-four hours to the minute after the fight in front of the Cézanne cinema, a Mrs Beatrice Lalland, who was not a marginal but a hard-working and respectable cleaning woman, looked out of the window of the Brasseur Furniture Company and saw that something was burning on the other side of the car park in front of the building.

Mrs Lalland could not see what it was because there was a heavy screen of bushes and small trees surrounding the car park and the fire was on the other side of them, but she assumed that it was a group of adolescent vandals engaged in destroying someone's property.

Being a woman with, perhaps, more courage than common sense, she shouldered the mop which she had been applying to the floor of the closed furniture store and marched stoutly out to intervene.

Intervention was no longer possible. Upon pushing

her way through the bushes, Mrs Lalland saw with amazement and horror that what was burning was a woman. Her hair and clothing had already burned away and the flames were rising from the seared flesh itself.

Mrs Lalland possessed solid nerves, but, when the police arrived in response to her near-hysterical telephone call, they found her sitting in a Louis XIV chair in the store, shaking over her entire body and weeping like a child. Her mop lay at the edge of the screen of trees where she had dropped it.

The first police unit to arrive had, of course, been a patrol car, but it was quickly followed by half a dozen cars and vans from the department of criminal investigations and a contingent of uniformed officers, who formed a cordon around the scene of what was soon determined to be a particularly vicious murder.

The fire had, by now, died down and there were only a few trails of smoke rising from the blackened flesh, so Dr Gerard Dunoyer, the department's squat, dark and beetle-browed medical expert, was able to begin his examination of the corpse immediately.

The cause of death, the doctor reported, had apparently been strangulation, for there was a woman's partially melted plastic belt still drawn tightly about the victim's neck. To the relief of all present, he was quite positive that the woman had been dead for at least an hour when she was set on fire at around nine that same evening.

Otherwise, there was nothing that he could determine at the scene. It was possible that something of interest might turn up with the autopsy.

Inspector Jerome Credoux, the stocky, black-moustached chief of the duty homicide squad, who had been called away from his dinner table, asked if there were any open wounds on the body. His assistant, Detective Sergeant Pierre Paule, had found traces of blood on the macadam paving eleven feet nine inches from the corpse.

The doctor replied that he could see no wounds and,

after having examined the traces of blood, remarked that they appeared to be mixed with some other secretions and so fresh that they almost had to be associated with the murder. He had certain suspicions, but he was unwilling to express an opinion until he had made tests.

'Make them,' said the inspector.

The doctor took samples of the blood and other substances and, while the specialists from the police laboratory began going over the area in search of potential clues, was driven back to headquarters to begin his tests.

He had not been there long when the inspector arrived. The specialists had found a plastic reserve cannister which contained petrol, but nothing else of significance and, although the investigations were continuing, he did not think they were going to find much more.

He had, therefore, left the sergeant in charge and come to find out what the doctor had determined with his tests.

The doctor said the tests had confirmed his suspicions. The blood and other secretions were from the womb of a woman giving birth.

'You mean somebody was having a baby while the murder was taking place?' said the inspector incredulously.

'Simultaneously or very near it,' said the doctor. 'Strange, isn't it?'

'Oh not at all,' said the inspector with exaggerated sarcasm. 'Kill one. Have a replacement immediately. Population balance. Anything else?'

'I can't say until I've received the corpse for the autopsy,' said the doctor a little stiffly.

'They'll be sending it to the morgue any time now,' said the inspector. 'I'm going back to my office. Let me know if anything significant turns up.'

Nothing significant turned up, either at the scene of the crime opposite the furniture store at 38 Avenue Brossolette or at the autopsy. All that the doctor could determine was that the woman had been rather badly beaten and scratched and that she had had treatment for her injuries.

'Meaning that they were not incurred at the time of the murder,' said the inspector.

'Seems a strange sequence to me,' remarked Sergeant Paule. 'The woman was beaten up. Then, some time later, she was strangled to death. Then, still later, she was set on fire. Were these things connected or not?'

He was a tall, loose-limbed, young man with a clean-shaven, open face and an earnest expression.

'What I want from you is answers, not questions,' said the inspector. 'I can think of enough questions myself. Get somebody from the identification section to go over to the morgue and try to get prints off the corpse. I wouldn't be surprised if she turns out to have a record.'

'What makes you think that?' asked the sergeant, who felt that the best way to learn the criminal investigation business was to ask questions.

'She was probably a prostitute,' said the inspector. 'Dunoyer says she was in her middle-thirties and would have been attractive when she was alive.'

The inspector's theory turned out to be incorrect. Although the identification specialists were able to recover identifiable fingerprints, the police had no record of them. Hélène Thomi had been charged, but the charges had been dropped and she had not been fingerprinted.

'Well, try the hospitals and doctors' offices then,' said the inspector. 'According to Dunoyer, she was treated for her injuries shortly before death. See if he can say exactly when and get a precise list of the injuries. Whoever treated her should be able to recognize them.'

Four hours later, the sergeant had a positive identification. The duty emergency hospital's records of Mrs Hélène Thomi's injuries, for which she had been admitted on the day before her murder, corresponded to the injuries established by the autopsy.

As the hospital records listed the cause of the injuries as assault, a police investigation had been obligatory and the sergeant was soon able to locate the detective who had taken Mrs Thomi's statement and obtain his report on the case.

Although this was not very useful as Mrs Thomi had provided no description of her assailant, it did contain one valuable piece of information: the number of the patrol car which had been called to the scene.

The officers were summoned, and they told the inspector what they knew of the matter – which was not much. The fight had been over by the time they arrived. Some of the spectators had said that the pregnant woman at the scene had been involved, but they had not actually seen her fighting. She and her companion had been marginal types who looked as if they had been rolling around in the street anyway.

The young man, late teens or early twenties, they thought, had been high on something, heroin probably.

'Very significant,' said the inspector. 'The victim has a fight with a pregnant woman that sends her to the hospital and twenty-four hours later she is murdered while somebody gives birth next to her. It would be one of the great coincidences of criminal investigation history if those two events were not connected.'

'Seems likely they would be,' agreed the sergeant, 'but I can't see that it helps us much if they are. If the woman was having a baby, she couldn't very well have strangled Mrs Thomi.'

'But she could have been a witness,' said the inspector.

'Maybe not,' said the sergeant. 'Maybe she was just pregnant and passing by and she came upon the burning corpse and it gave her such a shock that she went into labour.'

'Damn it, Pierre,' said the inspector mildly. 'That's an all too logical explanation. We may have to go at this from a different angle.'

'I can't think of any,' said the sergeant.

'I can,' said the inspector. 'What about motive? People kill people for a reason. It may not be a good reason or even one that makes much sense, but for the murderer, it's a reason. Now, why would anybody want to murder Mrs Thomi, maybe beat her up beforehand, and burn her body?'

The sergeant thought it over.

'No reason in the world,' he said finally. 'She wasn't a prostitute, so it wasn't her pimp or some business rival. She was on public assistance, so she didn't have any money. According to the records when she was charged, she preferred adolescent boys, but she would sleep with anything that looked like a human being, so it could hardly be an affair of the heart. Whoever killed her must have been completely mad, or he mistook her for someone else.'

'Possible, of course,' said the inspector, 'but, on the basis of the estimated time of death and the time when she was released from the hospital, the murderer would almost have had to meet her at the door when she came out, and that means he knew she was in the hospital. Check with the nurse and see if she had any visitors.'

The sergeant checked. Mrs Thomi had had a visitor, a young woman in the last stages of pregnancy.

'I thought it was her sister,' said the nurse. 'She was very affectionate toward the patient and there was a sort of family resemblance.'

'The pregnant woman again,' said the inspector. 'We've got to find that pregnant woman. There can't be any further doubt that she was mixed up in the murder in some way or other.'

'She's not pregnant now,' said the sergeant. 'She presumably had the baby at the scene of the crime.'

'Then she would have gone to see a doctor, at least,' said the inspector. 'Run a check of the city's physicians and maternity clinics and see who was admitted that evening. I'll see what I can do about tracing any sisters of Mrs Thomi.'

*

154

Hélène Thomi having been on public assistance, the inspector encountered little difficulty in obtaining information concerning her background as the social welfare authorities maintained records on their clients.

However, Hélène had been an only child. A native of Marseille, eighty miles to the south-west, she had been married once to a handicapped war veteran, by whom she had had a daughter named Marie-Ange, who was her closest living relative.

The social welfare office had no information in Hélène's file concerning the whereabouts of her daughter. The Thomis had divorced when Marie-Ange was three months old and the child had been raised by a paternal aunt. According to the records, she would have turned eighteen on 15 June that year.

The inspector, suspecting that he was now on to a valid lead, personally made the trip to Marseille to talk to the paternal aunt, who said that she was not at all surprised to learn that the police were interested in Marie-Ange and that the juvenile department of the social welfare service undoubtedly knew more about her than she did.

Marie-Ange, she said, had been precocious in every respect. She had been sexually promiscuous from the age of ten and probably before, both with boys of her own age and with adult men. She had been involved with drugs for nearly as long, but the aunt thought that she was not seriously addicted. She had been drunk as often as she could obtain enough alcohol in any form for the purpose. She had scarcely attended school at all, had no profession, had never held a job and lived in hippie communes or in the buildings occupied by squatters.

This unflattering description of Marie-Ange would later be confirmed by the social workers in the juvenile department who said, however, that they felt that Marie-Ange was basically a good person and that they expected eventually to make a useful member of society out of her.

The inspector did not see fit to comment on this project. What interested him was the information he had received from the aunt regarding Marie-Ange's relationship to her mother.

The girl, said the aunt, was morbidly fascinated with Hélène and convinced that she was a great sorceress. She thought that her mother was sitting in Aix-en-Provence continually casting spells to destroy her, and she was terrified of being bewitched.

Although she hated her bitterly for having abandoned her when she was three months old, she also seemed to love her and yearn for her love. At intervals, she would go to Aix-en-Provence and follow Hélène about in the streets for days on end.

Sometimes, she would be so overcome by her emotions that she would rush forward to kiss her mother and then fall upon her with fingernails and fists in a sort of panic-stricken effort to destroy that which she loved, hated and feared.

The aunt knew all about this as the juvenile department was invariably called in and social workers would come around to reproach her for failing to provide the loving care and nest warmth which they felt Marie-Ange needed.

As the aunt's control of the situation approximated that of a hog on roller skates, she was very bitter and indignant over these reproaches and did not consider herself to have any responsibility whatsoever for her ward.

She did not, she said, even know if Marie-Ange was in Marseille and, what was more, she did not care.

Marie-Ange was not in Marseille. When the inspector returned to Aix-en-Provence, the sergeant was waiting with the information that he had located the pregnant woman in the maternity ward of the same hospital where Hélène Thomi had been treated for her injuries.

'And you won't believe this,' he said, 'but her last name is the same as the victim's!'

156

The inspector believed it. He was not even surprised.

'I trust you've got her under surveillance,' he said. 'I think the woman killed her mother.'

The sergeant had not thought it necessary. Marie-Ange had given birth to a seven-pound daughter, tentatively named Natalie Thomi as she had no idea of the identity of the father, at nine-thirty in the evening of 21 June, and he thought it unlikely that she would attempt to flee with a new-born infant in her arms. In any case, he had not believed her to be a suspect in the murder nor did he believe her to be one now.

The inspector immediately corrected the situation by stationing a detective outside the door of Marie-Ange's room. This proved to be a wise precaution for, in a sense, the sergeant was right.

No more maternally inclined than her mother, Marie-Ange would not attempt to flee with the baby, but without it. The escape attempt was foiled by the detective and, as soon as the hospital would let him, the inspector began interrogating his unlikely suspect.

The interrogation was, by then, more of a formality than anything else as the inspector already knew the details of the crime and had two further suspects in custody.

The first of these was Marie-Ange's companion on the day of the fight in front of the Cézanne cinema. His name was Robert Boucher. He was twenty years old, unemployed, unwashed, uneducated and heavily addicted to heroin or anything else that would produce a high. Although he lived in abandoned buildings and earned his living by begging, he described himself as a surrealist artist.

Robert had been arrested when he came to visit Marie-Ange at the maternity ward and had proved very cooperative, immediately confessing to his part in the murder and naming the other participants. Although not particularly public-spirited, he had little interest in what happened to him or anyone else and found answering questions less tedious than continued interrogation.

The third suspect, fifteen-year-old François Lebeau, was equally cooperative and told essentially the same story as Boucher. Marie-Ange had asked him to help kill her mother and, as she was a friend who had introduced him to the joys of sex some two years earlier, he did not see how he could refuse her.

Even Marie-Ange cooperated with the police, saying that she had not only murdered her mother, but she felt she had performed a useful public service. The woman had been a great sorceress and heaven only knew how many people she had harmed with her spells.

She had, she said, become concerned over her mother's nefarious activities during the first part of June as she noted the approach of her eighteenth birthday, and she had resolved to put an end to them.

She and Robert had been squatting peacefully in Marseille with various friends and having a good time, but she could feel the baleful influence of her mother reaching down from Aix-en-Provence and she knew that she was seeking to destroy her.

She had, therefore, come with Robert to Aix-en-Provence on 15 June and celebrated her birthday by getting drunk and following her mother about in the streets.

She had not actually spoken to her until that afternoon in front of the Cézanne cinema when, unable to control her emotions, she rushed forward, kissed her on the cheek and sank her fingernails into her throat.

It had been Marie-Ange's intention to kill Hélène on the spot, but the spectators interfered and the murder had to be postponed.

She then sat down with Robert to think of a plan, but Robert being under the influence of something or other almost permanently, he found it difficult to think at all. The plan had, therefore, she stated with some pride, been entirely her own.

158

She would find out which hospital Hélène had been taken to and visit her, proclaiming repentance and a desire for reconciliation. She would propose to meet her mother when she was discharged and accompany her home. On the way there, they would kill her.

Robert found the plan brilliant and was all in favour of it, but pointed out that neither he nor Marie-Ange was in very good physical condition and he thought it doubtful they would be able to carry out the murder unassisted.

There was no denying the logic of this objection and Marie-Ange, casting about for a more sturdy helper, remembered François Lebeau, who was living, she thought, in Aix-en-Provence and should be in better physical shape than Robert, as she had only initiated him into the free life some two years earlier.

François was quickly located and, when told the plan, simply said, 'I'm with you.'

These preparations having been made, Marie-Ange set off for the hospital, where she assured her mother that she was a changed person and would love and care for her in the future. She would be waiting with friends to escort her home when she was discharged that evening.

Inexplicably, Hélène Thomi accepted this offer and, when she found Marie-Ange, Robert and François waiting for her outside the hospital that evening, she unsuspectingly went off with them, possibly reassured by the presence of two young boys, in view of her preferences.

Arriving at the screen of bushes around the car park, Marie-Ange gave the pre-arranged signal and the three adolescents fell over the victim, knocking her to the ground. Then Marie-Ange and Robert attempted to strangle her manually while François held her feet.

This was somewhat effective and, after a very considerable effort, Hélène lost consciousness.

Robert and François began congratulating their friend on her successful matricide, but Marie-Ange, having heard somewhere that sorceresses were extremely difficult to kill, pressed her ear to her mother's breast and heard the sound of her beating heart.

Crying out that the job was not yet done, she removed Hélène's belt, wrapped it around her throat and, handing one end to Robert, instructed him to pull with all his might while she did the same with the other end.

This proved successful and, after a time, no further sounds of a heartbeat could be heard.

Even then, Marie-Ange was not satisfied. A sorceress, she said, had to be burned or she was not really dead. She proposed that they burn her.

Robert and Francois had, however, become nervous. Talking about a murder was one thing. Finding yourself with a corpse was another. If there were no stirrings of contrition in their drug-ravaged minds, there was the beginning of fear of what consequences this act might have for them personally.

They voted against the burning, pointing out that they had nothing with which to set the corpse on fire anyway. Instead, they suggested that they all go off and have a good meal in a restaurant to celebrate a great deed well done.

Marie-Ange reluctantly agreed. François had recently received an allocation from the welfare office to further his education, although he was not actually enrolled in any school, and the funds necessary for the dinner were at hand.

They were also adequate to cover a good deal of wine, which so cheered the spirits of Robert and François that they agreed after dinner to go and burn up the corpse.

They stole a reserve cannister from a car and siphoned off a gallon or two of petrol with a rubber tube which Robert carried around for such purposes.

Returning to the scene of the crime, they doused the body liberally and set it on fire, but, as they were about to leave, Marie-Ange, understandably stimulated by the sight of her mother's corpse in flames, went into labour and barely missed giving birth on the spot.

The faithful Robert and François carried her off to the hospital where they had picked up her mother earlier that evening, and she had finished having her baby there.

The defence at the trial made a great deal of the youth and innocence of the defendants, all now suitably washed and sober. These children, cried the attorneys, were not criminals. They were victims of an unfair society. If sent to prison, their young lives could be ruined. If released and given counselling, they could be saved to become useful members of society.

These appeals might have been more effective had the prosecution not pointed out that all three defendants, even Marie-Ange, had had good, comfortable, middle-class homes and the opportunity to proceed as far in their schooling as they wished or were able. They had voluntarily chosen a life of drugs, promiscuous sex, idleness and, finally, murder. The fact that Marie-Ange had sincerely believed her mother to be a sorceress was no excuse for murdering her.

The jury also thought not, but they did accept that there had been certain extenuating circumstances. Marie-Ange was given the modest sentence of twenty years' imprisonment. Robert received fifteen and François, despite his youth, twelve. All should be out in less than ten years.

Is murdering and burning up your mother deviate behaviour?

Few would describe it as normal.

12

KEEPING IT IN THE FAMILY

Bad Soden is not a place where anyone would expect to find great numbers of deviates.

Or non-deviates either, for that matter.

A community of barely eight thousand permanent residents on the outskirts of the West German city of Frankfurt am Main, it owes its existence to the mineral springs found there and the beauty of the surrounding landscape.

People in need of rest and a cure in allegedly healing waters come to Bad Soden, but in modest numbers, for it is not one of the great spas and has no casino.

The visitors sometimes find Bad Soden a little too restful.

For the local residents, it can be more exciting.

On 22 October 1976, the excitement in Bad Soden began with the discovery of a corpse.

Thirty-eight-year-old Erwin Dreyser, strolling along the banks of a drainage ditch bordering his farm on the outskirts of the village, spotted the body at a little before two in the afternoon and, even though he could not see the features, immediately recognized that it was a stranger. Dreyser had been born and raised in Bad Soden and he knew every person there by sight, even floating face down in the water.

The discovery puzzled the farmer greatly. Having dug the ditch himself, he knew that the water in it was no more than three feet deep in any place and all that anyone who had fallen in needed to do to escape drowning was to stand up. Granted that the banks were rather steep and high, they would present no serious obstacle to an adult.

There was, however, no time to ponder the mystery. Here was a fat man lying in his drainage ditch, and the thing to do was get him out if he had not yet drowned.

Dreyser, therefore, plunged courageously down the bank and into the water, where he managed to turn the man over on his back and drag him over to the edge.

As he had expected, it was a stranger, a man in his late forties whom he had never seen before, but he realized with consternation that he was not only dead, but had been dead for some time. The body was not stiff, but it was cold as ice and there was no sign of respiration.

Dreyser left the body where it was and hurried home to telephone the town constable. He was not a big man himself and the corpse was very large and heavy. It would have been impossible for him to get it up the bank alone.

It was impossible with the aid of the constable as well. Only after a second farmer had been summoned could the body be dragged up the steep bank and laid out on level ground.

'Must be a visitor,' said the constable in dismay. 'Something like this is bad for Bad Soden. How could the damn fool manage to drown himself in a drainage ditch?'

'Must have been drunk out of his mind,' said Dreyser. 'I've said for years they ought to have more entertainment here. The visitors sit around watching television and drink themselves unconscious. That's no way to run a spa.'

Like most European villages, local politics were fiercely contested and Dreyser belonged to the party currently out of power.

'Don't blame the village council,' retorted the constable. 'They can't make a night club out of the place.'

He had been appointed by the party in power.

'Can't do anything else either,' said Dreyser sourly and went off in the direction of his house.

The constable, who did not want to leave the corpse alone for fear that a passing stray dog might eat part of it, immediately deputized the second farmer and ordered him to remain with the body until he could summon an ambulance to take it to the local undertaker. Bad Soden has no morgue.

Nor any ambulance. The village being within sight of the Frankfurt city limits, it makes use of the larger city's facilities for the few emergencies that occur.

The ambulance, therefore, came out from Frankfurt, but the body was taken to the police morgue in Frankfurt and not to the local undertaker, as the Bad Soden coroner refused to issue a death certificate.

'We not only don't know how he managed to drown like that,' he said. 'We don't even know who he is.'

'His name's Jan Fryderyk Fischer and he comes from Duisburg,' said the constable. 'His identity card was in his pocket. He was fifty-one years old.'

'And not registered at any of the hotels here,' said the coroner. 'So what was he doing in Bad Soden?'

The constable could not reply, and that same afternoon Detective Sergeant Max Higler came out from the Frankfurt department of criminal investigations, talked to the constable and a number of other persons and then went through the residents' registry in the mayor's office.

There were four Fischers listed. The name is common in Germany. The sergeant noted their addresses and set out to call upon them.

He got the right Fischer on his third call. Forty-two-year-old Daniel Fischer, who lived less than a hundred yards from the drainage ditch where the body had been found, said that he had a fifty-one-year-old brother named Jan Fryderyk who lived in Duisburg, but he assumed that he was still there.

The sergeant took him in to the morgue in Frankfurt,

where he made an official identification of the corpse. Jan Fryderyk was not, it seemed, in Duisburg.

Daniel wept copiously and said that his poor brother had, no doubt, been coming to visit him and fallen into the ditch. He was, he said, almost continuously drunk, which would explain how he came to drown in three feet of water.

Which was, according to the autopsy, how he had died: by drowning and while unbelievably drunk.

'The level of alcohol in the blood was the highest I have ever seen,' said Dr Ludwig Becker, the tall, balding police medical expert who had performed the autopsy. 'If he hadn't drowned, he would have stood a good chance of dying of alcohol poisoning.'

He was sitting in the office of Inspector Walter Grumann, Sergeant Higler's immediate superior, absently polishing his horn-rimmed glasses and reporting his findings. The official autopsy report was in the process of being typed up.

'Liver like a sponge, I suppose?' said the inspector. A dark, intense, hyper-active little man who was often described as dynamic, he was not very interested in a drunk drowning in a drainage ditch. What he preferred was a really spectacular murder case which was good for the career.

'As a matter of fact, no,' said the doctor. 'No indications at all of chronic alcoholism. He was in exceptionally good physical shape for a man of his age and weight.'

'Then why was his blood full of alcohol?' asked the sergeant, who had been listening to the report from his desk in the corner. 'Are you saying that he fell in a ditch and drowned the very first time he got drunk?'

'Of course not,' said the doctor. 'He could have been drunk a good many times before it did discernible damage to the organs. All I'm saying is that he wasn't an alcoholic.'

'How much would you say he drank before he

drowned?' asked the inspector, becoming a little more interested.

'The equivalent of an entire bottle of whisky, brandy, vodka or any other distilled spirits,' said the doctor. 'I didn't run stomach-content analysis. Should I?'

The inspector hesitated. 'Go ahead,' he said finally. 'And, Max, take a run back out to Bad Soden and at least find out where he did his drinking. It must have been in Bad Soden itself because he wouldn't have been able to go very far afterwards.'

The doctor went back to the morgue and the sergeant set off cheerfully for Bad Soden. He was a big man, blond, loose-limbed and slightly clumsy like a St Bernard puppy, and he preferred the outdoors to the office. Frankfurt was its usual grimy, noisy, polluted self, but, in Bad Soden, the air would be clear and crisp and the mixed forests around the little town would be a glory of red and gold autumn leaves.

There being a limited number of places in Bad Soden where alcohol was available, it did not take the sergeant long to determine that Fischer had not done his drinking in any of them. It was not a time of year when there were many visitors and a stranger, particularly one of Fischer's size, stood out.

No one, it seemed, had even seen him on the day on which he had drowned, Tuesday, 19 October, according to the autopsy, and it was a mystery as to how he had got out to the edge of town. No car had been found so he had, apparently, been on foot.

Meaning, the sergeant reasoned, that he had arrived in Bad Soden by train or by bus and, if so, perhaps he had taken a taxi.

There were only four taxis in Bad Soden and three of these had had no large, plump, male, non-resident fare on 19 October.

The fourth had not either, but only because he had refused him. Thirty-four-year-old Oscar Beisel told the sergeant that he had been summoned to the house of

Daniel Fischer in Koenigsberg Strasse on the afternoon of 19 October. Daniel and his thirty-eight-year-old wife, Marian, had been outside with a large, plump stranger between them. They had asked Beisel to drive the man to the hospital in Witzenhausen.

Beisel had not liked the look of the proposed fare at all. The man's head was lolling forward on his chest and he appeared to be unconscious. The Fischers were having a hard time holding him up. Beisel had recommended that they call an ambulance and gone back to his stand.

This testimony made the case so serious that the sergeant took Beisel back to police headquarters in Frankfurt so that he could make a formal statement there.

'In short,' said Inspector Grumann, now much more intrigued, 'the brother made a deliberate false statement to you. Suspicious, very, very suspicious.'

'That's what I thought,' said the sergeant. 'But why? Even if Daniel Fischer tossed his brother into the ditch when he was unconscious drunk so that he drowned, we couldn't prove it. Why didn't he simply say that Jan Fryderyk had been to visit him and left full of booze to the eyes? The coroner would almost surely have issued a death certificate naming accidental drowning as the cause. The ditch has steep banks and the autopsy did show that he was drunk as a coot.'

The inspector thought it over.

'He didn't want an investigation,' he said finally. 'And he was too stupid to realize that there would have to be one anyway. There must be something in his relationship to his brother which would make it obvious that he would have had a motive for murdering him.'

'Can't imagine what it would be,' said the sergeant. 'Duisburg is close to two hundred miles from here and Jan Fryderyk wasn't a frequent visitor, because nobody in Bad Soden knew him by sight.'

'You don't need to imagine,' said the inspector,

'because you are going to find out or, at least, I hope you are. As of this moment, the death of Jan Fryderyk Fischer is classed as suspected homicide and you are in charge of the investigation. You can start by finding out what the relationship between the brothers was.'

'Openly?' said the sergeant. 'Can I bring Fischer in for questioning?'

'Not if you plan to continue working in criminal investigations,' said the inspector. 'Fischer is to suspect nothing. We don't want him covering his tracks any more than he's already covered them. You're to be discreet, very, very discreet.'

The sergeant did not think that it would be possible to be very, very discreet in Bad Soden and, in any case, no one there had known the victim. He therefore drove up to Duisburg, which is in the Ruhr district some one hundred and eighty miles to the north.

Jan Fryderyk's identity card had listed him as married and his wife's maiden name as Antonie Boell. She was six years older than her husband and, when the sergeant finally located her, it turned out that he was not her husband any more. She had, she said, filed for divorce the preceding year and it had become final in May of 1976.

'Why?' said the sergeant. 'You were married for a long time?'

He knew that the couple had a fifteen-year-old daughter named Esther.

'Twenty-seven years,' said the former Mrs Fischer tersely. 'I don't want to talk about it.'

'Mrs Fischer . . .' began the sergeant.

'Boell,' said Mrs Fischer.

'Mrs Boell,' said the sergeant patiently. 'I am engaged in investigating a suspected homicide. We have reason to believe that your husband may have been murdered. Withholding information in connection with the investigation of a felony is an offence punishable by law and, if you refuse to cooperate, I shall have to take you back to Frankfurt to be questioned and, possibly, charged.'

'What do you want to know?' said Mrs Boell.

'Nothing about your relationship to your former husband,' said the sergeant. 'Only about his relationship to his brother in Bad Soden, Daniel Fischer.'

Mrs Boell reflected.

'The two things are connected,' she said finally. 'I can't tell you about one without the other.'

'Then, Mrs Boell,' said the sergeant, 'I am afraid you are going to have to reveal all.'

'Well, I suppose you'd find it out anyway,' said Mrs Boell. 'It's in the records of the divorce proceedings. I just wanted to spare Esther.'

'Your daughter?' said the sergeant, beginning to feel that he understood the situation. 'Your husband was . . .?'

'Not with Esther,' said Mrs Boell indignantly. 'Although I don't doubt that the swine was capable of it. With his niece.'

'Daniel's daughter?' said the sergeant. 'How old is she?'

'Twenty now,' said Mrs Boell, 'but this has been going for a long time. Since the little bitch was nine, I understand.'

'Your husband was having sex relations with his nine-year-old-niece for the past eleven years and you only divorce him now?' said the sergeant wonderingly.

German housewives do not, as a rule, call police officers idiots, but Antonie Boell looked the word at him.

'Not Jan Fryderyk,' she hissed. 'Daniel. Her own father. Jan Fryderyk only got in on the act last year. He and Daniel were estranged. They'd hardly seen each other in twenty years. Then that hussy came round telling Jan Fryderyk that her own father was abusing her and could he help. You bet he could help. He brought her up here to Duisburg and installed her in our house. Of course, she was in bed with him almost before the door closed behind her. Insatiable little tart!'

The sergeant had found what he had been sent to find. An overwhelming motive for murder.

'I'm afraid I'm going to have to ask you to step down to police headquarters here to make a statement, Mrs Boell,' said the sergeant. 'This is a little more complicated than I thought it was.'

The case was, indeed, more complicated than anyone would have had reason to expect and, although Antonie Boell did not know all of the details, she knew enough to make a highly interesting statement.

The situation was not, however, as bad as it had originally appeared. There had been no actual incest. Mechthild Kiel was not Daniel Fischer's daughter, but the daughter of his wife, Marian, whose maiden name had been Kiel. The identity of the real father was not known.

According to the statement by Mrs Boell, her husband had brought Mechthild home with him on the afternoon of 7 June 1975 and told her that the girl had appealed to him for help as her stepfather was forcing her to have sex relations with him.

'She did not look like she needed much forcing,' said Mrs Boell grimly, 'but she was Jan Fryderyk's niece by marriage at least so I didn't throw her out of the house.

'It was a mistake. Within a day, I realized that Jan Fryderyk had a different idea of help than I did, but before it came to anything, Daniel showed up here in Duisburg and there was an awful row, which ended in his taking Mechthild back to Bad Soden with him.

'I thought that was the end of it, but no, a week later, Jan Fryderyk went down to Bad Soden and brought her back up here.

'He was crazy about her and she was completely shameless. If I hadn't been there, I think they'd have done it in front of Esther.

'There were some terrible scenes, but, again, before anything was actually settled, Daniel came back with a regular commando. There were three or four of them and they practically carried Mechthild off by force. Jan Fryderyk said they were armed.

'Even after that, he wouldn't give up and he went running down to Bad Soden and brought her back, I don't know how.

'I'd had enough and I told him that it was either Mechthild or me.

'He said, "All right. It's Mechthild." And they left together.'

'I filed for divorce, and the only time I've seen him since was in court. Esther is with me, of course.'

Esther Fischer was with her mother in more senses than one and confirmed in a separate statement to a woman officer of the juvenile section everything that Antonie had said, adding certain details which the outraged wife had either been spared or which she had been unwilling to repeat.

As for the sergeant, having collected the statements on the affair and checked the records of the divorce court, he went back to Frankfurt in happy anticipation of startling his chief out of his executive-type chair.

If the inspector was startled, he managed to conceal it masterfully.

'About what I expected,' he said. 'The trouble is, we can't ask for an indictment on the basis of a motive and nothing else. Maybe it really was accidental. Maybe Jan Fryderyk got roaring drunk to drown his sorrows and drowned himself along with them. We can't prove it wasn't that.'

'You want me to drop it then?' said the sergeant hopefully. He did not care very much for the case.

'Not at all,' said the inspector. 'Where's your sense of duty? Fischer was murdered. It's up to you to collect the evidence to bring the murderer to justice.'

The sergeant went glumly off to do so, idly wondering a little how difficult it would be to get himself hired at some other city's department of criminal investigations.

The only comforting aspect to the whole affair was that the inspector had now given him a free hand to act as he saw fit.

He promptly made use of this freedom of action by taking into custody both Daniel Fischer and his wife and subjecting them to hard interrogation. As far as he was concerned, there was no point in continued discretion.

While this was going on, he sought out Mechthild Kiel, who had now, it seemed, run away and was living with a male non-relative. He asked her to make a statement.

She really was a remarkably attractive girl and, like Mrs Boell, she said she did not want to talk about it.

The sergeant then recited his piece about withholding information in connection with the investigation of a felony, but, unlike Mrs Boell, Mechthild said he would first have to prove she had any such information, and she still didn't want to talk about it.

This matter being settled, the sergeant went back to headquarters, where he learned that Daniel was still insisting he knew nothing about his brother's death and denying his relationship to his stepdaughter had ever been anything other than paternal. However, Marian had given up and was telling everything she knew, which, it seemed, was really everything.

She was, she said, aware that her husband had been having sexual relations with her daughter from about the age of nine, but the only complaint Mechthild had ever made was, in recent years, that Daniel was getting a bit old and sluggish. He had not forced her and she could have put a stop to the business any time she wanted.

She did not know why Mechthild had run off to her uncle, but she thought she had probably simply wanted a little change. She had never, to her knowledge, had intimate relations with anyone outside the family and seemed much attached to her older relatives. Or even older persons to whom she was not related. The man with whom Mechthild was now living was forty-six.

In any case, said Mrs Fischer, there had been a terrible tug-of-war between the two brothers over the girl which lasted for months and, when Jan Fryderyk came down to Bad Soden on 19 October, Daniel decided to put an end to it and him too.

He had apparently planned this in advance, for he told her two days earlier to buy a large bottle of brandy with the highest alcohol content she could find. When Jan Fryderyk turned up and began whining about Mechthild, Daniel pointed a shotgun at him and ordered him to drink the whole bottle of brandy neat.

Jan Fryderyk refused and Daniel produced a whip to beat him into submission.

This was not necessary as the sight of the whip proved sufficiently convincing, and Jan Fryderyk drank the entire bottle.

He then became semi-conscious and Daniel, apparently getting cold feet, told Marian to call a taxi and they would send him to the hospital.

The taxi, however, refused to accept him and Daniel led him off and, she supposed, pushed him into the ditch. She had not actually seen him do so.

Confronted with his wife's confession, Daniel Fischer added his own and, for good measure, incriminated two others: Johannes Kiel, his thirty-four-year-old brother-in-law, and a cousin, twenty-six-year-old Erich Becker.

The two had accompanied him on the commando raid to Duisburg, and Kiel, at least, had been present at the time of the murder. As he was her brother, Mrs Fischer had thought it better not to mention this.

All of these statements and confessions having been duly recorded and neatly typed up, indictments were handed out all round and, three months later, on 21 January 1978, a court found the defendants guilty of homicide and acting as an accessory to homicide, and sentenced Daniel to life imprisonment, Johannes Kiel to twenty years, Marian Fischer to six years and Erich

Becker to nothing as he appeared to have had no knowledge of the crime.

It can, of course, be argued that neither Daniel nor Jan Fryderyk was guilty of deviate behaviour.

After all, neither was related to Mechthild by blood and, if she was a trifle young at the beginning of the affair, well, the Dutch parliament is at this moment pondering the lowering of the age of consent to twelve, so why not nine? On that basis, their conduct was normal.

But what about Mechthild's behaviour?

13

NEVER TRUST ANYONE OVER SEVENTY

Not so very far to the north and a little to the west of Bad Soden, where Mechthild Kiel wrought havoc within the Fischer family, lies the German Westerwald which, although perhaps not internationally famous, is regarded with affection by many Germans.

An ancient mountain chain, now worn down to low wooded hills, steep stone outcroppings and swampy valleys, it enjoys the romantic appeal of Sherwood Forest as bands of revolting peasants once made their head-quarters there.

The Westerwald is a favoured site for campers in summer, but few choose to live there permanently. The climate is severe, with heavy snowfalls in winter and extreme humidity all year round.

On the Easter weekend beginning 5 April 1980, the Westerwald was as humid as ever, but, as the campers expected nothing else, they came anyway. The sun was shining and it was warm by German standards, which are spartan generally but exaggerated in the country's several million campers.

Already by Friday evening the camping site at Heimborn-Ehrlich on the Nister river was so filled with caravans and camping cars that there was not room left for so much as a pup tent. Groups of adults drank beer, played cards and generally enjoyed themselves. The playground swarmed with children.

Saturday was no different. More beer was drunk, more cards were played, sausages were consumed, people went for walks, the children romped and shrieked in the playground, located a hundred and fifty yards from the campsite to spare the ears of the adult campers.

On Sunday, thirteen-year-old Beate Lohmann disappeared.

Exactly when was not possible to determine. A pretty, almost alarmingly well-developed girl who looked considerably older than she was, she had had lunch with her parents, Dora and Gerd Mechtel, outside their caravan and then gone off down the road in the direction of the playground. Beate might look eighteen, but she was still a little girl and she liked to play with the other children.

Beate's last name was not the same as that of her parents because Gerd was not her father. Mrs Mechtel had been previously married and divorced.

Gerd was, however, as attached to Beate as Daniel Fischer had been to Mechthild, although in a much different way, and, when she failed to appear for dinner at six-thirty, he went off to look for her.

Beate was not at the playground and he was unable to find any children there who had seen her at all that afternoon. Alarmed and concerned, he hurried back to the caravan to tell his wife, who immediately joined him in the search.

There is much solidarity among Germans, particularly among campers, and it was not long before the entire camp was searching for Beate.

They did not find her, but they did receive some frightening reports from other children. Four of them said they had seen Beate either getting into a green car or already in a green car. Unfortunately, they were all young children and they were not sure of the make of car. Three said it was an Opel. One said it was a Renault.

At the moment, the make of the car was not as important as the fact that Beate had been in it at all.

Being a little girl in West Germany today is a very high-risk condition indeed. More than twenty years of lenient treatment of criminals in general and sex criminals in particular has left the country swarming with convicted rapists, child molesters and even murderers. A little girl or even a little boy stands in need of survival training.

And Beate had had it. Her parents had drummed into her ears from the moment that she could understand the language that she was never, never, never, under any circumstances, to go with a stranger, no matter who he said he was or even if he was wearing a uniform; she was never to get into a car unless her mother or father were in it and she was even not to put too much faith in her own family members. Over fifty per cent of sex offences against children are committed by relatives of the victim.

The Mechtels could not, therefore, believe that Beate had got into the green car of her own will, and no sooner had they heard the children's reports than they hastened to telephone the police.

The nearest police station was in Altkirchen, which is a community of under five thousand inhabitants and has a police force of corresponding size.

The entire force came out to the campsite, but they could not find Beate either. Even more conscious of the dangers to children in a modern, progressive society than were the Mechtels, they wasted no more time and called in the department of criminal investigations from the city of Koblenz, the largest community in the area, with a population of over a hundred and twenty thousand.

The Koblenz police took the matter as seriously as the officers from Altenkirchen and, by Monday, the entire area was filled with police, off-duty firemen, units of the German army and volunteers.

They were not really looking for Beate any more. They were looking for her body, but they did not find that either.

The search continued for a week and was then called off. Helicopters had criss-crossed the forest and failed to sight anything. Trained tracking dogs had sniffed articles of Beate's clothing and failed to pick up any trail. The searchers had combed every patch of brush thick enough to hide a body and skin-divers had gone over the bottoms of the ponds and lakes. Beate was not there. Alive or dead, she was no longer in the area.

The Nister river had, of course, always been considered a possibility, but it was relatively fast-flowing, which made it hard to say how far downstream a body might have passed in the length of time before the full-scale search began. Both banks had, however, been scoured for a distance of two miles downstream from the camp, but without result.

'He probably didn't want to chance disposing of the body near the camp,' said Inspector Karl Schoenherr of the criminal investigations department of the Koblenz police. 'He drove straight out of the district once he had her in the car. The only hope is that he may simply be holding her somewhere.'

A very experienced officer within five years of retirement, the inspector, stocky, hard-bodied and with iron-grey hair and a drooping moustache, had been assigned overall direction of the case as he was something of a specialist in offences against children.

'She could be better off dead,' said his assistant, Detective Sergeant Paul Feldner.

A tall, painfully thin man with a long, dark face, he was inclined to pessimism and had often found good reason for the attitude in the past.

'He wouldn't be holding her for ransom. The Mechtels don't have that kind of money. And she's too old for him to ever release her. She could identify him.'

'We'll release her,' said the inspector, but, privately he was not optimistic.

'Could have been a white-slaver,' continued the sergeant gloomily. 'The North Africans are taking them younger all the time. She'd even be a little too old for some of them, but she was pretty and . . .'

'Oh knock it off, Paul,' said the inspector mildly. 'If you want to indulge in groundless speculation, at least speculate about something cheerful. Did you ever hear of a white slaver kidnapping a child from a campsite where there were hundreds of people around at the time?'

'Four little kids saw it,' said the sergeant. 'Nobody else. He's probably torturing her to death right now, dragging it out as long as possible to get his kicks. You remember the Pfortzer case? What that fellow did . . .?'

'Get out,' said the inspector. 'Go and investigate something. I don't care what.'

He did not like remembering the Pfortzer case. The girl in that had been even younger and it had happened over five years earlier, but neither he nor the sergeant would ever forget it.

That was the trouble with working so long together as a team, he thought. You were always reminding each other of things that it was better to forget.

As the case neared the end of the second week with still no trace of the missing girl, even the inspector was inclined to doubt that either Beate or her body would ever be recovered. As the murderer had transport, the body could be anywhere in Germany. It was not a large country, but there was still plenty of room to hide a child's corpse in it.

As it turned out, however, Beate had not left the area in a car, but by water. Nearly twenty miles downstream from the camp site at Heimborn-Ehrlich there is a dam across the Nister and, as there is some traffic on the stream, there are locks.

Locks require a lock keeper, and on the morning of 20 October Arnold Kraemer came out of his neat little lock keeper's cottage and found Beate Lohmann floating at the top of the dam.

Kraemer did not immediately realize that it was Beate as she was inside a gunny sack which had been tied at the mouth with cord. However, whatever was in the sack, it had no business floating around behind the dam, and Kraemer got a boat-hook and towed it over to the bank.

By the time he had done this, he had come to the conclusion that he would not try to get it out of the water. Beate had been in the sack for exactly two weeks and the odour of rotting flesh was quite noticeable.

Even so, it did not occur to Kraemer that the contents might be an adolescent girl. He had heard of Beate's disappearance, for it had been in all of the newspapers and on the radio and television newscasts, but he simply failed to connect the information to this stinking sack. Instead, he thought someone had butchered a hog and thrown the offal into the river.

As a result, Kraemer nearly passed the sack through the lock to let it go on down the river and, had he done so, it is possible that no one would ever have known what happened to Beate Lohmann, with the exception of two persons who were not likely to reveal their knowledge.

Attempting to get the sack into the lock, Kraemer found that it was remarkably heavy, too heavy to be simply the unwanted parts of a hog and, holding his nose with one hand, he cut the cord closing the mouth of the sack with his pocket knife.

The sight revealed left him utterly mystified.

Beate had been put into the sack doubled up with her feet nearly touching her shoulders. It was, therefore, her naked buttocks which lay framed in the open mouth of the sack and it was several minutes before Kraemer, who had never seen anyone from such an angle in his life, could work out what they were.

Even when he did, the thought of the missing Beate Lohmann did not cross his mind and his near-incoherent call to the police merely stated that there was a dead woman in a sack in the river.

Beate Lohmann did, of course, occur to the police. Inspector Schoenherr, Sergeant Feldner and a sleek, plump, gold-rimmed bespectacled medical expert named Martin Eisenhauer arrived at the scene in under an hour.

The body was still in the river, but Kraemer had attached it with a line to the boat hook, which he had driven into the mud so that it would not float away again. He himself was in his cottage drinking neat brandy. A shy, mild-mannered man, his discovery had largely unnerved him.

It came close to unnerving such hardened characters as the inspector and the sergeant, but the doctor was not troubled at all. Corpses were his business and this was one, even if it was in poor shape.

'Would be in worse shape yet,' he said almost cheerfully, 'if it wasn't for the water being so cold. She won't smell much once we get her out of the sack.'

The inspector did not, however, want to take the girl out of the sack.

'This is no place,' he said. 'Who knows what clues might be lost here in the mud? We'll take her in to the morgue, sack and all.'

The sergeant was very much in favour of this solution. He did not want to take the girl out of the sack either, and it was obvious that there was no one to do it except himself and the inspector.

Somewhat over the doctor's objections, as regulations called for an examination of the corpse as found at the scene, the sack was pulled on to the bank and the sergeant went off to telephone for an ambulance.

In the meantime, the inspector took a statement from Arnold Kraemer and decided not to carry out any investigation at the scene. The body had obviously floated down the river to the dam, and there would be nothing for an investigation to uncover.

As the ambulance had to come out from Koblenz, there was a wait of some forty minutes. The inspector walked unhappily up and down the bank of the river, while the sergeant sat smoking and staring glumly through the windscreen of the police car and the doctor poked about in the sack.

The victim being in an advantageous position for a gynaecological examination, he soon called out to the inspector that the girl had been raped and that she had previously been a virgin.

The inspector did not reply or cease his pacing. He had expected nothing else and he did not feel like making conversation. Although he was a specialist in such cases, he hated murders of children. He had fathered two daughters himself and, although they were now grown women with children of their own, he still remembered them as little girls.

Despite the inspector's caution over removing the body from the sack, no clues were found in or on it. The police laboratory reported that it was an ordinary gunny sack, such as was used for storing potatoes and other things, and that it was untraceable.

Beate's clothing was also in the sack and on her, with the exception of her panties, which had been ripped off, but there was nothing about them to indicate the identity of the murderer.

The autopsy report was more informative. Beate had been hit on the back of the head with what had probably been a large stone. It had fractured her skull and undoubtedly dazed her, but it was not the cause of death.

The cause of death was drowning. Beate had been rendered helpless by the blow to the head, raped, put into the sack alive and perhaps conscious and thrown into the river to drown.

'About as brutal a procedure as I've encountered,' said the inspector grimly. 'How did the identification go off?'

The sergeant had had the unpleasant duty of bringing the Mechtels to the morgue for the official identification of their daughter.

'She looked good,' said the sergeant. 'Eisenhauer did a fine job cleaning up the face. Mrs Mechtel fainted.'

'Small wonder,' said the inspector. 'Well, let's get on

with it. I've asked the records section to give us a print-out on known sex offenders who attack adolescent females, and you can start a detail sorting and checking immediately. Almost surely somebody on the books. The thing was too brutal and deliberate to be a first offence.'

'If he's from this area at all,' said the sergeant. 'What about the kids who saw her get into the car? Do you think we can get anything more out of them?'

'We'll try,' said the inspector. 'I'm going to show them pictures of cars and see if we can get an identification of the make at least.'

The investigation therefore set off in two different directions simultaneously and, gratifyingly, both produced results.

The children who had seen Beate either getting into or already in the car were able to agree on a picture of a 1976 model Opel, and the little boy who had originally suggested a Renault was even able to come up with two letters of the licence plate.

Assuming that he was not mistaken, the car had been local, for German licence plate numbers indicate the city in which the car is registered and the letters were those used for Altenkirchen.

A six-year-old girl, the only one of the four witnesses who had seen Beate getting into the car, said that she thought she had been pulled in and that she had been trying to get away. It had been the driver who was pulling, but there was also another man in the back seat.

On the basis of this information, the investigators began a search of the records of the vehicle registration office in Altenkirchen.

In the meantime, the search of the police records for known sex offenders with a history of attacks on adolescent girls had resulted in a startlingly large number of potential suspects for such a sparsely populated district.

Having excluded the homosexuals who attacked only

boys, the impotent not capable of penetration and those with fixations on older or younger age groups, the sergeant still had eleven names on his list. All of these men had long records of sex offences against young girls, and each required individual attention.

Some could be eliminated immediately. Two were actually in jail. One was seventy-three years old. Another was in the hospital. Four had checkable alibis for the afternoon of the day in question.

In the end, three remained, but only one drove a green Opel and came from Altenkirchen. His name was Otto Fuchshammer; he was twenty-four years old, and six years previously he had raped and murdered a twelve-year-old girl, for which he had been given the maximum sentence possible under German juvenile law: ten years.

As usual, Fuchshammer had served less than half of his sentence, had been given some psychiatric counselling and released as a rehabilitated member-in-good-standing of society.

The Altenkirchen police suspected that he had raped at least two girls since then, but, as no charges had been preferred, he remained officially rehabilitated.

The only problem with Fuchshammer as a suspect was that his green Opel was not a 1976 model, but a nearly new 1980 model.

'Could the children have all made the same mistake in the model?' mused the inspector. 'They're young of course, but . . .'

'Not that young,' said the sergeant. 'There's a lot of difference in the appearance of the 1976 and 1980 models. It may have been Fuchshammer, but it wasn't the car he's driving now.'

'We'll try a line-up of green Opels and then we'll try a line-up with Fuchshammer,' said the inspector. 'Fortunately, the parents are cooperating.'

'And so are the kids,' said the sergeant, 'but what do you think a good defence counsel is going to do with an identification by four pre-school kids, even if it is all four of them?'

The inspector sighed. 'Tear it to pieces, of course,' he said. 'Do you have any better suggestion?'

The sergeant had no other suggestion at all and the line-ups took place. They were far from satisfactory to the investigators.

To begin with, all four of the little witnesses picked the 1976 model Opel which was not Fuchshammer's car.

Worse yet, none of the children picked Fuchshammer as the driver of the car. Two, however, said that he had been the man in the back seat!

'We're going to have to release him,' said the inspector in dismay. 'We're going to be accused of holding him purely on the basis of his past record.'

This was, as a matter of fact, exactly what Otto Fuchshammer had been saying ever since he was arrested, and the newspapers were beginning to agree.

'Do you think he really was the man in the back seat?' said the sergeant. 'The girl was raped by only one man, according to Eisenhauer, and, from what we know of Fuchshammer, he doesn't seem the type to let someone else do his raping for him.'

'He could be the man in the back seat and still be the rapist,' pointed out the inspector. 'There's no evidence that the driver was the rapist.'

'Maybe the driver has no previous record,' suggested the sergeant, 'and maybe . . .'

'. . . he drives a 1976 green Opel,' concluded the inspector. 'You may have it, Paul.'

But Paul did not. The vehicle registry records in Altenkirchen had produced a number of green 1976 model Opels, but none of the owners appeared to have any connection to Otto Fuchshammer.

Fuchshammer was released with not very sincere apologies from the police, and the inspector went back to poring over the files covering what had already been done in the case.

'There's one 1976 green Opel here that isn't checked off as investigated,' he called to the sergeant, who was typing up a report on another case at his desk in the corner.

'Belongs to the seventy-three-year-old man,' said the sergeant. 'He was eliminated because of his age. Couldn't have run the girl down, let alone rape her.'

'Ah, but don't forget there was another man in the car,' said the inspector, becoming slightly excited. 'I think we may have something here. What's the fellow's name – Maerzhaeuser – may have been the driver and the man in the back seat did the raping and murdering. Has Maerzhaeuser got a long record?'

'Long as your arm,' said the sergeant. 'Just a minute and I'll get you the file.'

Seventy-three-year-old Josef Maerzhaeuser did, indeed, have a criminal record nearly as long as the inspector's arm, but it was a rather monotonous one for, with the exception of a few convictions for theft, all of his offences were rape or attempted rape, mostly but not exclusively of adolescent girls.

'If the man were a little younger . . .' remarked the inspector. 'What does he look like? Is he in good shape?'

'He's a wreck,' said the sergeant. 'Looks ten years older than he is. If he's capable of rape, I'm capable of swimming the Atlantic.'

'You may regret that remark when you're doing the breast-stroke off the Azores,' said the inspector. 'I still say that he's a major suspect, if not as the actual murderer, then as aiding and abetting. There's too much against him. A life-long record of sex crimes against adolescents. A 1976 green Opel. A local man who knows the area. Bring him in. If he's half as feeble as you say he is, we shouldn't have much trouble interrogating the truth out of him.'

Unfortunately for the inspector's plans, Josef Maerzhaeuser was not feeble in the least. It was true that he was scrawny, mostly bald and badly wrinkled, but he

186

was as tough as leather, and all the inspector could get out of him were threats of a suit for false arrest and demands for legal counsel.

The inspector was not impressed. He had heard such threats before. As legal counsel was required by law, he provided it, but then took into custody Maerzhaeuser's sixty-six-year-old wife, Maria, and their eighteen-year-old son, Peter, an apprentice house painter. Maria and Josef were not living together. Peter and Josef were.

'Well,' said the inspector rather smugly, 'now we have a driver of a 1976 green Opel and a man for the back seat. Let us see if our four young witnesses can identify them.'

Three of the young witnesses could! The fourth was not so sure.

'Probably worthless in court,' observed the sergeant, 'but I'm convinced. Peter must be following in his father's footsteps. The old man took him out for his trial rape.'

Maria Maerzhaeuser disagreed. 'Nonsense!' she snapped. 'If anybody raped the girl, it was Josef. He's been doing it all his life. Peter's only eighteen. He can have all the adolescent girls he wants without raping them.'

There was some basis to this argument. Peter Maerzhaeuser was a reasonably attractive young man and the adolescent girls of the eighties were thoroughly liberated. There were many younger than Beate Lohmann who would not have died virgins.

None the less, it was Peter who was charged. The inspector still did not believe that a man of seventy-three, even with Josef Maerzhaeuser's vast experience, was capable of the savage and violent rape of a strong, healthy teenager.

His son insisted that he was. Weeping copiously, he led the police to the point on the banks of the Nister where, he said, the crime had taken place, not only in his presence, as he later admitted, but with his assistance.

187

He had not wanted to rape anybody. Nor had he expected that there would be any such activity when his father took him for a drive on Easter Sunday.

It had all happened very suddenly. They had been passing the girl, who was walking along the road in the direction of the playground, when his father abruptly stopped the car and dragged the girl into the front seat.

Beate fought and struggled, and his father ordered him to hold her still. He had done so because a good son owed obedience to his father and, anyway, he was afraid that the old man would beat him up.

When they arrived at the spot where the crime took place, Beate managed to get away from him, jumped out of the car and ran.

His father ran after her and, catching up a stone, threw it so accurately or so luckily that he hit her in the back of the head, knocking her to the ground.

The girl was dazed but not unconscious, and Josef ripped away her underwear and raped her on the spot while his son watched, horrified, or so he said.

The rape completed, Josef ordered him to get a gunny sack from the trunk of the car and, together, they pulled it over the half-conscious girl and tied the mouth with cord.

They then simply carried the sack to the river and tossed it in.

Josef Maerzhaeuser denied bitterly everything in his son's statement. The boy was lying because he was jealous of his success with women. He was probably a homosexual, which was why nobody wanted to have anything to do with him. As for Maria, she was jealous for the same reason. She was an old woman and she resented his love affairs with young girls.

Josef could not, however, name any of the young girls with whom he had had love affairs – out of a desire to protect their reputations, he said. The jury not only did not believe this, but hardly anything else he had to say.

On 3 July 1981, Josef Maerzhaeuser was found guilty

of rape and murder and sentenced to life imprisonment. As he was now seventy-four-years-old, it was, presumably, a short sentence.

Peter Maerzhaeuser did not come out of the affair very well either. Being a juvenile, the maximum that he could receive was ten years, and that was what he got for aiding and abetting rape and murder.

14

AN ALL-ROUND MAN

The corpse was a horrifying sight. It lay face down between the rows of ripening corn, and the blood from the lacerated scalp had filled the plastic sack fastened with cord around the neck. Protected from the air, the blood had not congealed or lost its colour, so that the head looked like a plump red child's balloon.

Yves Belfontaine, a resident of Saint-Seine-en-Bache, rather more given to exercise than the average Frenchman, turned pale and narrowly escaped losing his lunch.

It would have been a pity, for the lunch had been a good one and, following it, Belfontaine, who was in comfortable circumstances and did not hold a job, had decided to take a walk. It was not exactly that he had a weight problem, but it was still always well to keep things within bounds.

He had not expected to see many other strollers in the country lanes outside the little town. It was a Friday, 3 September 1982, and nearly everyone would be at work. Saint-Seine-en-Bache, being rural and agricultural, did not have as high a rate of unemployment as some other parts of France.

Now, Belfontaine wished that there were more people about. He had averted his eyes immediately he realized what he was seeing, but he had no doubt the man was dead. That hideous red balloon where his head should have been was guarantee enough for that.

Backing out of the cornfield, Belfontaine hurried along the paths between the fields until he caught sight of a farmer working in the distance and began waving his arms, jumping up and down and shouting at the top of his lungs.

The farmer, at first inclined to run from an apparent madman, fortunately recognized Belfontaine and came to investigate.

Half an hour later, Captain Denis Serrault of the Dijon Gendarmerie, was made aware that another homicide had taken place in the so-called Triangle of Death.

The title was an invention of the press, who used it to describe what was thought to be a series of rapes and murders, most of which had taken place within an area bounded by the communities of Besançon, Dole and Lons-le-Saunier. All had taken place within the past three years. None had been solved.

The captain, a brisk, businesslike olive-skinned man with fine features and large slightly slanted dark eyes, was not pleased to learn that someone had been murdered, but he was relieved the anticipated murder had now finally taken place and the gendarmerie would have another chance to identify the murderer.

According to the theory, the victim of this new Triangle of Death crime would be a young blonde woman and she would have been raped. With few exceptions, all previous victims had answered to this description and the killer was believed to be a sex psychopath with a fixation.

To the captain's dismay, this latest victim did not match the pattern at all. He was young and he had been raped, but he was not a blonde woman. He was a dark-haired soldier, six feet four inches tall and muscled like a cart-horse.

'An unusual sex object for a rapist,' remarked Dr Charles Bressaud, the medical expert attached to the criminal investigations section of the Dijon Gendarmerie, 'but apparently a stimulating one. He achieved orgasm inside the anus. Cause of death was probably head wounds. I can't say for certain until I remove the sack and I don't want to do that until I have the body in the morgue.'

'Right,' said the captain. 'Can you give me an estimate on the time of death? I want to know if we should set up road-blocks.'

'No need,' said the doctor. 'He's been dead since yesterday afternoon at least.'

'Keep an eye on things here, Jerome,' said the captain. 'I'm going back to the office. Let me know immediately if the laboratory people find anything.'

'Jerome' was Sergeant Jerome Poiron, the captain's silent, hulking, slightly sinister assistant officer-in-charge. 'The laboratory people' were the specialists and technicians attached to the gendarmerie laboratory who were now on their way to the scene and who would go over the area by the square centimetre in the hopes of finding some clue to the murderer's identity.

The captain was anxious to get back to his office as he wanted to institute a check by the records section of known homicidal homosexuals capable of raping six-foot-four soldiers. He did not think there would be many.

There were none.

'You must remember, however, that the case near Troyes the other day involved a homosexual rape too,' said the chief of the records section. 'He raped the wife first and then the husband. Granted, the victim was no six-foot-four athlete, but he was definitely male.'

'You think then that it could be the same man?' said the captain. 'The psychologists said he only raped the man because he was stimulated by the rape of the woman. She was young and blonde and so was the husband.'

The records chief shrugged. 'No idea,' he said. 'I only keep track of them. You and the brain mechanics will have to work out who they are and why they do it.'

The captain did not find this very helpful and went back to his office slightly out of sorts. It was all very well to say that it was up to him to work out the identity of the killer, but how was he to do that, if there were never any clues?

Actually, there were some clues, including a reasonably accurate description of the man who was probably the killer by the young couple he had raped.

According to them, he was a serious, respectable-looking man in his late twenties or early thirties. He had a pleasant manner, wore his hair short and stylishly cut, dressed well and neatly and drove a maroon Volkswagen Rabbit.

He had picked up the husband and wife, both blond and long-haired and neither twenty years old, as they were hitch-hiking outside the city of Troyes, which, like Dijon, is in the east of France, but somewhat more to the north.

The couple thought him a square, some kind of a businessman or civil servant.

He turned out to be businesslike enough and even reasonably civil, but far from square in his attitudes.

Turning into the first forest road leading off the main highway, he drove in far enough for privacy, produced a gun and ordered the couple to strip.

They were indignant, but had done so. The man looked dangerous now and, it being 28 August, the weather was not unsuited for nudity. As they admitted to the gendarmes, they had not been too upset at the prospect of sex with the man. He was clean and presentable, and they were a modern, liberated couple.

The man then attached the husband to a tree with cord which he took from the trunk of the car and raped the wife, laying her across the front seat of the car and standing in the open door.

The process did not take very long and the couple assumed that they would now be released.

To their surprise and consternation, the man attached the wife to the tree and, holding the gun to the back of

193

the husband's head, bent him over the hood of the car and raped him anally.

This did not take very long either and, when it was finished, the psychopath took the husband to the tree and tied him next to his wife.

He then looked at them speculatively, weighing the gun in his hand, and the couple had the terrifying impression that he was trying to decide whether to kill them or not.

Apparently deciding against it, he finally got into the car and drove away.

The badly shaken couple had not been tied too securely and were soon able to free themselves. Getting back into their clothes, they resumed their hitch-hiking, but in the direction of Troyes, where they reported their experience to the police.

This being rape and threat of homicide within the Triangle of Death area, the report was immediately passed on to Captain Serrault, who had been in charge of the investigations since 12 September 1979. He was not at all happy about it.

The affair, the captain now reflected, sitting at his desk with the great mound of files representing the various cases nearly covering it, was beginning to have an unfortunate effect on his career. The press was becoming increasingly critical of the lack of progress in solving the murders and his superiors, sensitive to the political implications, were beginning to put a great deal of pressure on him. If the investigation were to be taken out of his hands, he could expect to retire with the rank of captain, if that.

This latest crime could be crucial, for it was basically different from those preceding it. It would tend to support the captain's private theory, which he had not revealed even to the sergeant, that what they were dealing with was not a single series sex criminal, but two or more such sex psychopaths operating in the same area and at the same time.

194

The captain suspected this theory would not be popular with his chiefs. It gave the impression that the country was swarming with homicidal sex maniacs. But it would explain why the gendarmerie efforts had, so far, been fruitless. The indications were unclear and the clues were contradictory because the crimes had not been committed in all cases by the same man.

Sighing, the captain opened the file of the case which had begun the series and which had been, in his opinion, the worst crime of all.

It had taken place on 12 September 1979, almost exactly three years earlier, in an open forest on the outskirts of the town of Dole, less than twenty miles to the south-east of Dijon.

On the afternoon of that day, twenty-three-year-old Yvonne Crosby had gone for a walk with her six-year-old daughter Lydia. Both were blonde, with long, straight hair.

They had never returned, and those who had gone to seek them eventually found mother and child naked, dead and disfigured. Yvonne had been raped.

Both victims had been stabbed repeatedly and beaten around the head with some heavy object, thought to be a hammer or the back of a small hatchet.

There was not the slightest clue to the identity of the murderer other than his semen in the body of the young mother and the obvious fact that he was a seriously deranged compulsive sex psychopath.

Such meager indications were not enough and, although Captain Serrault's men interrogated practically every soul living in Dole, a community of some thirty thousand inhabitants, no witnesses were ever found.

Murders such as those of Yvonne and Lydia Crosby are nearly always series crimes as the forces which drove the murderer to kill once will cause him to kill again. The classic response is to wait reluctantly for the next murder or rape in the hope that this time there will clues or witnesses.

The tactic had not worked in the Crosby murders. From 12 September 1979 to 1 May 1982, there had not been a single comparable crime in the entire east of France where it could not be shown that the perpetrator was not the murderer of Yvonne and Lydia Crosby.

The captain had done his best and he had failed, but there was no reason for criticism. Many criminal cases lack the information to make a solution possible. Gendarmes are not expected to work miracles.

May first of 1982 had really signalled the beginning of the captain's sorrows.

On that date, three months before the soldier's death, a twenty-five-year-old blonde woman of Eastern European extraction named Kaija Elena Koivvoja had been found dead near the town of Lons-le-Saunier, one of the points of what would later become the Triangle of Death. As there were certain parallels to the murder of Yvonne Crosby, the case was assigned to Captain Serrault.

The captain was convinced that it had been the sex psychopath for whom he had been waiting ever since September of 1979. The victim had been stabbed, stripped, raped and beaten about the head with something heavy and hard. The semen recovered from the corpse was that of a man with the same blood group as in the Crosby case.

Unfortunately, there was another parallel. There were no clues and no witnesses.

Or, at least, there had been none so far. The case was by no means closed and the investigation was continuing on 2 September when the young soldier had been raped and murdered in the cornfield.

It was not, however, the only investigation, for there had been a fourth murder, on 23 August.

It had taken place near the city of Besançon, forty miles to the east of Dijon and another of the points of the Triangle of Death.

196

The victim was a pretty woman with long, straight, blonde hair. She was twenty-three years old and her name was Andrea Kowe.

Like the other victims in the presumed series, Miss Kowe had been stripped, raped, stabbed and beaten about the head with a hard object. The blood group of the rapist corresponded to that determined in the other cases.

Blood group, of course, meant nothing. There were literally millions of persons with the same group. It was not really an indication.

Nor were there any others. The killer was either remarkably clever, remarkably cautious or remarkably lucky.

The captain was, perhaps, clever, but he was neither cautious nor, it seemed, lucky. He had barely started the investigation into the Kowe murder when the rape of the husband and wife took place.

More personnel had had to be assigned to that and, now the Crosby case had been reactivated on the basis of the more recent crimes, the captain found himself with four investigations going on simultaneously.

It was, perhaps, gratifying to be entrusted with so much responsibility, but it was also a dangerously exposed position for a civil servant and he felt himself far too vulnerable.

Now, it seemed, a fifth investigation was to be added and the captain was wondering just how many parallels there would be to the other cases. On the basis of what he now knew, there did not appear to be many.

The specialists from the gendarmerie laboratory reported with the monotonous regularity which had characterized their previous reports that they had found nothing at the scene which might be useful in identifying the murderer.

The victim had been identified. He was nineteen-year-old Christophe Breton, who had been performing his compulsory military service at Besançon. He was last seen setting out to hitch-hike back to his base from a visit home. Although hitch-hiking was known to be dangerous, Breton had not thought that he had much to fear. On the contrary, his size made it difficult for him to get rides.

But, unfortunately, not difficult enough. According to the indications at the scene and the findings of the autopsy, Breton had been brought to the cornfield in a car, marched into the corn, presumably at gunpoint with his hands tied behind his back, and had been raped anally where the body lay. His skull had been fractured with what was thought to be the butt of a pistol before the plastic sack was drawn over his head and tied around the neck. Breton had actually drowned in his own blood, although the autopsy showed that the head injuries were so serious they would have resulted in death in time as well.

The victim was not a blonde female. The cause of death did not include stabbing. There was little to tie the crime to the Triangle of Death murders other than the location.

There was much to tie it to what the captain now thought was the second series of rapes and murders overlapping in time and space the Triangle of Death cases.

On 15 August, a nineteen-year-old German hitch-hiker named Karl Bulcke had been found dead at the edge of a small forest near the town of Rochefort-Montagne. He had been raped anally and executed with a single twenty-two calibre bullet fired into the nape of the neck at point-blank range.

With the exception of the anal rape, the case was not remarkable. In August, France was full of hitch-hikers, foreign and domestic, and equally full of perverts waiting to pick them up. When these participants met, the case often became of interest to the homicide squad.

The matter probably would not have come to Captain

Serrault's attention at all, had it not been for the fact that there was a second, almost identical crime on 19 August which had taken place in the Triangle near Lons-le-Saunier. Rochefort-Montagne is close to four hundred miles to the south-west.

The victim in this case was French, a sixteen-year-old boy named Christian Klein. He too had been hitch-hiking. He too had been raped. He too had been shot in the neck with a twenty-two calibre weapon.

The double rape of the husband and wife had not yet taken place, and what Captain Serrault was looking for were cases involving the rape and murder of young blonde women. Therefore, it had not been included in the Triangle of Death file and the investigation was left to the gendarmerie station at Clermont-Ferrand, which was handling the Bulcke murder.

The soldier's murder appeared to fit these two murders better than any of the captain's cases. He was about to transfer it to the Clermont-Ferrand investigators when he was handed one of the lucky breaks that sometimes occur in a criminal investigation.

On the afternoon of 4 September, two days after the soldier's murder, a gendarmerie patrol car was stationed at the edge of State Highway E2 running from Dijon to Dole. The officers in it were watching for stolen vehicles for which they had a list of licence numbers.

Presently, a car bearing one of the listed licence numbers passed and the gendarmes set out in hot pursuit.

The chase was short. No sooner had the officers switched on the siren and set in motion the flashing revolving lights on the roof of the patrol car than the stolen vehicle slowed and pulled over to the side of the road.

The gendarmes approached cautiously. The penalties for murdering a police officer were not very severe in socialist France and other officers had approached other stolen cars to be met with a hail of bullets.

As it turned out, the driver was armed, but he was in such a state of abject terror, his teeth literally chattering and his entire body shaking violently, that he would have been in greater danger of shooting himself than anyone else.

In what was, perhaps, a record time for a confession, he gibbered at the astounded gendarmes that he was the notorious Hitch-hiker Murderer.

The title was another invention of the press and referred to the murderer of Karl Bulcke, Christian Klein and, more recently, Christophe Breton.

The delighted gendarmes drew their pistols, ordered him of out of the car, searched him, confiscated a twenty-two calibre long-rifle pistol, handcuffed the blubbering killer and brought him to gendarmerie headquarters in Dijon. There he was rushed to the department of criminal investigations, cautioned on his rights and interviewed personally by Captain Serrault.

Purely on the basis of appearance, twenty-one-year-old Pascal Bertrand was not a very satisfactory suspect. He was thin, frail, pimpled, wore glasses and was so painfully timid that he answered the captain's questions in a near-inaudible whisper.

In other respects, he was more suitable. He knew exactly where the bodies of Karl Bulcke and Christian Klein had been found. He knew exactly what he had done to them before he had murdered them. He did not know their names, but, as he shyly pointed out, that had not been necessary for his purposes. Many of the details that he described had not been released to the press and were known only to the police and the murderer.

Finally, there was physical evidence as well. The gun found in Bertrand's possession had been taken to the gendarmerie ballistics section for test firing and the slugs from the heads of the victims compared with the test bullets. They matched perfectly.

Without doubt, the captain had solved the murders of Karl Bulcke and Christian Klein for the Clermont-

Ferrand gendarmes, but, from his own point of view, he had solved the wrong cases.

Pascal Bertrand denied vigorously having had anything to do with the murders of Christophe Breton, Yvonne and Lydia Crosby, Kaija Koivvoja or Andrea Kowe and, as the penalty for seven murders was no more severe than the penalty for two, there was no reason why he should not be telling the truth.

The captain believed him, although he did not want to, but the press did not and splashed headlines everywhere to the effect that the Triangle of Death Killer had at last been trapped.

Captain Serrault knew better, and on 23 September, only nineteen days after the arrest of Pascal Bertrand, he was proved right.

Twenty-year-old Leon Guichard, another soldier serving his compulsory military service, was hitch-hiking home to spend a long weekend when he was picked up by a man driving a maroon Volkswagen Rabbit. The man was in his early thirties, reasonably good-looking, neatly dressed and conventional in his manner.

He drove Guichard to a forest near the town of Venarey-les-Laumes, put a pistol to his head and raped him anally.

Guichard wisely offered no resistance, which undoubtedly saved his life and made it possible for him to provide Captain Serrault with another detailed description of the Triangle of Death Killer as well as the licence-plate number of the car.

This latter proved valueless. The car had been reported stolen a month earlier in Bayonne, which is in the extreme south-west corner of the country and about as far from Dijon as it is possible to get and remain in France.

The knowledge was, however, disconcerting. The killer did not confine his activities to the Triangle of Death. He might strike anywhere and, indeed, Venarey-les-Laumes was not inside the Triangle itself, but thirty miles to the north-east of Dijon.

It was, none the less, definitely the killer or, at least, the killer of Christophe Breton and the rapist of the young married couple, for there was physical evidence connecting the crimes.

In all three cases, the victims had been bound with thick white cord, and the gendarmerie laboratory was able to establish that these cords were identical and cut from a single length.

This was an important conclusion, for the captain now knew that he was dealing with one man in all three cases and, the witnesses in two of these cases having survived, they could, perhaps, recognize a picture of their aggressor. The gendarmerie psychologists were unanimous in the opinion that the killer would have a police record.

Guichard, therefore, spent several days poring over the police mug books of known sex offenders, not only for the region, but for all of France.

The married couple had already done this and failed, but they had only seen pictures of sex offenders from the region. It had not been known at that time that the killer was moving about the country.

Things went better with this new approach and Guichard was able to identify one of the pictures as being that of the man who had raped him. The picture was then included among a few dozen others and the married couple also picked it out as being that of their attacker.

The Dijon gendarmes now not only knew the identity of the Triangle of Death Killer, but they knew a good deal about him as well.

His name was Daniel Baron. He was thirty-two years old. He came from Perreux, a town three hundred miles to the south of Dijon. He was dangerous.

Baron had apparently always been dangerous. Although he completed an apprenticeship as a cook, he had never worked at any place for longer than three months. Unstable, bisexual and unpredictable, he was believed to have committed a number of aggressions and sex offences for which he had not been charged.

Baron enlisted in the French Foreign Legion for five years, but proved to be no more suited to military life than to cooking. After three years he deserted and returned to France where, on 15 June 1974, he kidnapped a fifteen-year-old boy at a village fair near the town of Limoges and entertained himself with him sexually for three days.

At the end of that time the boy escaped and was able to identify Baron, who was arrested in Hermies, a village in the north of France, on 17 July.

Following a closed trial and testimony by state-appointed psychologists to the effect that Baron was extremely dangerous and could not be allowed to mingle with the public, he was sentenced to ten years' imprisonment and taken to the prison in Einsisheim, on the eastern border of the country.

Theoretically, Baron should have remained in prison until 1985, but, as is common in many places today, the prison authorities had the power to alter the findings of a court and they granted Baron leave from the prison on 13 March 1982.

Baron promptly disappeared and was arrested only two months later in the Drome region, where he then remained – at the prison in Valence.

Despite this escape attempt, Baron was still judged to be a potentially useful member of society by the penal authorities, who released him altogether on 11 August 1982.

Looking at this record, a number of things became obvious to Captain Serrault. To begin with, Baron could not be responsible for the murders of Yvonne and Lydia Crosby, for he had been in jail at the time. Ominously, however, he had been a fugitive from justice at the time of the Kaija Elena Koivvoja murder, and the rest of the crimes believed to be connected with the so-called Triangle of Death had all taken place after his release.

Baron was, without doubt, the right man, and only one important question remained.

Where was he?

He could be anywhere in France, but, on 27 September, he was actually in a small, pleasant town, with the somewhat unpleasant-sounding name of Berck, on the Channel coast not very far to the south of Calais.

He was still driving the stolen Volkswagen Rabbit and he parked it in front of a café frequented by students from a nearby lycée.

Entering the café, he introduced himself as Michel Beauvois, a director of the second national television chain. He was, he said, looking for adolescents to take part in a television programme for the sum of two hundred and fifty francs a day.

As Baron was well-dressed, clean and perfectly respectable in appearance, none of the students had the slightest doubt concerning the validity of his proposition and he was swamped with so many candidates that he literally could not make up his mind. The only fair way to settle the matter, he announced, was to draw straws.

This was done, and to a handsome youth who had apparently offended the gods in some way fell the fatal choice.

Rejoicing greatly, he went and climbed into Baron's car. He was within minutes of rape and, perhaps, death when he was saved by a fifteen-year-old girl named Hélène whose greatest ambition was to appear in television. Flinging herself upon the killer, she pleaded pitifully to be allowed to come along too.

Baron was bisexual. 'Well, if you insist,' he conceded generously.

Hélène, in raptures, went off to tell her father where she was going so that he would not be searching for her. Baron was fully in agreement as he did not want anyone searching for her either.

204

When Hélène returned, however, it was with her father, who was not so impressed with working for television and who thought he would like a look at this television director.

A large, athletic man, he asked to see Baron's papers. Baron replied easily that he had left them in the hotel. 'What hotel?' said the father.

Baron could not name one.

The nineteen-year-old boy in the car had been listening and now left the vehicle hurriedly. Baron got in and drove away.

But not before the suspicious father had had time to note down the licence-plate number, which he immediately telephoned to the Berck police.

It was a very wanted number anywhere in France and, within minutes, road-blocks were going up throughout the district.

Baron was not intercepted at any of them, but late that afternoon the car was spotted parked in front of a café and he was taken into custody as he came out.

Notified of the arrest, Captain Serrault and Sergeant Poiron hurried to Berck, where, after seven and a half hours of interrogation, Daniel Baron broke down and provided the gendarmes with a detailed account of his activities since leaving prison on 11 August.

He had been busy. He had stolen a car immediately, carried out a hold-up, stolen another car, raped and murdered Andrea Kowe, raped the husband and wife, swindled half a dozen hotels and restaurants, committed a number of thefts from department stores, raped and murdered Christophe Breton and raped Leon Guichard. He might, he pointed out, have overlooked a few things. A great deal had been crowded into a short space of time.

Daniel Baron was eventually tried, found guilty of many things and sentenced to life imprisonment. So too was Pascal Bertrand. The murderer of Yvonne and Lydia Crosby is still at large.

15

YOUTH! LIBERTY! PROGRESS!

Not so very long ago and not so very far away, there once lived a modern West German family named Hommerich.

There was Pápa Hommerich, who was a successful executive and who could afford a large car and several mistresses (some part-time only).

There was Mama Hommerich, who was blonde and pretty and athletic and very vivacious and who taught aerobic dancing at the high school in Attendorn, which was where all of the Hommerichs originally lived.

There were the three little Hommerichs, of whom Thorsten, the youngest, was the best loved and the most pampered.

The Hommerichs were all very modern, very progressive and very happy. They owned a fine home, two cars and an enormous colour television. A video recorder was not beyond their reach.

Alas! One day in 1978, Hannelore Hommerich found out about the several mistresses and promptly filed for divorce and a generous amount of maintenance.

Papa Hommerich had no choice but to pay. Mama had the evidence and bringing up three children was obviously going to cost something.

On the other hand, so was maintaining several mistresses, to say nothing of the Mercedes. Papa did not, therefore, pay any more than he had to and, as he was a shrewd businessman, he managed to keep the total outlay somewhat under the average combined wages for three semi-skilled workers on union scale.

Mama and the three little Hommerichs, who were by now not so little, Thorsten having been fifteen at the time of the divorce, were reduced to economies. There was only one Mercedes left for the entire family and little hope of a video recorder.

Mama responded gallantly, taking on more aerobic dancing classes, and no one actually went hungry or naked (except by choice and then only in the house). It was possible for the two oldest young Hommerichs to complete their schooling and take up their rightful places in the production chain society.

For this purpose, they had to leave Attendorn, for there were few links in the production chain in that modest community of under twenty-five thousand inhabitants, located forty miles to the south-east of the great industrial complex of the Ruhr.

They left. They did not return. Until the funeral, for which they remained only briefly. They have no place in this story and that is the last that will be heard of them.

Not so Papa Hommerich, who was in the police detention cells at the time of the funeral, desperately trying to remember where he might have been on the afternoon and evening of 20 October 1983 and who would swear to it.

Thorsten was not in the detention cells nor in Attendorn either, but at his apartment in the village of Lenhausen some eleven miles distant from Attendorn. Now twenty years old and a fine, upstanding figure of a youth, he was known to his intimates as 'Wuschl', a German ephithet applied to persons with particularly abundant red hair.

Thorsten, or Wuschl, had an astonishing number of intimates because he was very successful both financially and socially.

A boy who kept an eye on the trend, he had begun by hating his father either when he found out about the mistresses or, perhaps, when he learned that the maintenance would not extend to his having his own car *and* video recorder.

This was socially correct in Germany in the seventies and eighties. Up-to-date young people were supposed to hate at least one parent and, if possible, both – an idea which originated in the United States, where a number of journalists had made some money out of it and passed on to other ventures.

However, as in Arabia, where the dogs bark and the caravan passes, in America the writers bark and the trend passes.

In Germany the trend does not pass. Failing to understand the commercial nature of trend promotion, young Germans often tend to regard an American effort to turn a quick buck as a bona-fide wave of the future.

Throughout the eighties, young Germans were busily hating their parents when, with the exception of the usual percentage of freaks, the most recent generation in the United States would have found the idea so old-fashioned as to cause death by humiliation.

However, as it is hard work and inconvenient hating both parents, many young Germans settle for hating one and love the other dearly. This was the case with Wuschl, who loudly cursed his father in public places and proclaimed his love for his mother when he was drunk, which was not often as it is dangerous to drink when you are on hard drugs.

Wuschl was, of course, on hashish, but mostly cocaine. He was, after all, a normal youth and he had been assured by the press that narcotics were no worse than alcohol or tobacco or even coffee. They were, in fact, better because they were modern and up-to-the-minute.

Unfortunately, it is difficult to concentrate on your studies when you are in orbit on coke, and Wuschl had not done well at school. In fact, he had done so badly that he had had to leave altogether.

This was not as tragic as it seemed, for Wuschl had

inherited his father's business acumen and it was already obvious that he would never have to hold a job. Cocaine is not cheap, but Wuschl could afford it easily, and the rent on the apartment in Lenhausen and a video recorder to boot.

Actually, that was about all there was in the apartment: a television set, the video recorder and two mattresses, one of which was reserved for guests. Wuschl often entertained.

The spartan furnishings did not, however, make the cost of living any cheaper and, short of actually working, there was only one means of obtaining such an income in Attendorn.

And Wuschl mastered it! By the age of twenty, the talented youth had made himself king of the drug traffic in Attendorn! It was an accomplishment of which no modern youth need feel ashamed.

At regular intervals, Wuschl made business trips to the great drug centre of Amsterdam in nearby Holland, where he was able to purchase a wide selection of narcotics at wholesale prices for resale at substantial mark-ups in his sales district.

Applying the time-honoured principles of promoting the product through advertising and free samples, he steadily expanded the demand and, at the time of his mother's funeral, was carrying well over a hundred satisfied customers on his books. None were adult. Some were still in elementary school.

A typical, modern success story to confound the pessimists who claim that the spirit of enterprise is dead in Europe.

And yet, for all his success, Wuschl did not forget his mother. He was often in his old room in the house at Hellepaedchen 32, playing his old hard-rock favourites on the record player, smoking a few joints and providing that warm sense of continuing family so necessary to a mother whose children are grown and children no more.

His friends came with him. Although all of his

customers were, by necessity, his friends, three were more intimate than the others and, if Wuschl was D'Artagnan, Heiko Vogel, Andreas Waschek and Sabine Ahrens were the Three Musketeers, although some jealous tongues also compared them to the Four Horsemen of the Apocalypse.

Actually, of the four, Wuschl was probably the only one who would have had the strength to climb on to a horse. Close to six feet tall and solidly built, he had not yet been so weakened by narcotics that he could not beat up a recalcitrant customer, and he looked the picture of wholesome, slightly dirty, health.

The other three did not look unhealthy either, although they were rather frail. The two boys were barely eighteen and Sabine had just passed her fifteenth birthday, so none of them had lived long enough for the narcotics to affect their physical appearance.

Which was, unfortunately, not really all that impressive. Heiko, who was theoretically undergoing an apprenticeship as a metal former, was nearly as tall as Wuschl, but skinny, and his narrow face was a sort of dirty-lemon colour beneath a modified dark-blond Comanche haircut. The red plush jacket which he habitually wore did not flatter him.

Andreas was also dark-blond, but wore his hair long over a low, badly wrinkled forehead in a fringe, through which he peered with dark, sunken, sorrowful eyes. As the rest of his face was covered with acne, he was anxious to grow a beard, but had, so far, not succeeded in doing so. When he worked, he was a motor mechanic. He did not work often.

Sabine was more attractive. Being an adolescent girl, she looked like one. Straw-blonde straight hair stretching to below her shoulders. A little, pouting, red mouth. Round, pink cheeks, plump with baby fat. For her age, she was astoundingly well-built and dressed to show it.

Sabine was another of the many victims of society. She had become addicted to a startling array of drugs by the age of twelve, so her parents had put her into an institution where she was supposed to undergo withdrawal and, presumably, cure.

Sabine was not in agreement with this and, tying her bed-sheets together, shinned down two storeys to the street and freedom.

After supporting herself and her habit by cut-rate prostitution (she lacked Wuschl's business sense) for some months, she had encountered the gallant Drug King. He scooped her up from the gutter, more or less literally, and carried her off to the apartment in Lenhausen, where she had remained ever since. Her parents knew that she was there, but they had given up and abandoned her.

It might seem that in Attendorn all of the ingredients for happiness were present. Papa Hommerich was busy with his Mercedes and his mistresses. Mama Hommerich was joyfully contorting her fifty-four-year-old but lovely body in healthful and lucrative aerobic dances. Young Wuschl had successfully launched himself into the world of business and was enjoying the loving admiration of his little circle of friends. Even the drug addicts were happy, assured of a reliable source of supply. Who could ask more?

Many of the young people of Attendorn, it seemed. There were, they complained, few opportunities for entertainment for young persons in the little town and, perhaps, there was some truth to what they said.

Less than a mile and a half from the city was the mighty Schnellenberg Castle, a picturesque thirteenth-century ruin with a chapel where couples from all over the country came to be married, but few of the Attendorn youth were interested in castles or in getting married either.

Otherwise, there was only the town square, which, except for two park benches and a bus stop, was as bare as a billiard table. Fronting on this expanse of neatly swept concrete were the recreational facilities: a solitary cinema, a stall selling French fries, an arcade with half a dozen pinball machines and a discothèque where cola cost four marks a bottle.

Drugs were actually cheaper. Although a joint cost twelve marks, the effect was more than three times as strong. Like any good businessman, Wuschl prided himself on quality. Cocaine was, of course, more expensive at three hundred marks a gram, but, if you wanted the best, you had to expect to pay for it.

The Attendorn youth seemed at least partially justified in their complaints and, as some organs of the press later pointed out, it was small wonder if they took to narcotics. They had been promised paradise as their right and all they had received was second-run films, pinball machines and soggy French fries.

Nor was it only the younger generation that was suffering. Hannelore Hommerich too was unhappy.

'Be reasonable, Thorsten,' she nagged. 'There's no future in the drug business. Sooner or later, the police are going to catch you and then you'll be in trouble. Why don't you take a course in accounting? You should learn a profession.'

'Mama,' said Thorsten patiently. 'I've told you repeatedly. I make in a week what an accountant earns in a year. And as for the police, there's one sergeant nearly due for retirement on narcotics and that's the whole squad for the Olpe district.'

Olpe was the district capital three miles to the south.

'I don't care,' said Hannelore stubbornly. 'I want you to get out of the drug business. If you don't stop it, I'll go to the police myself.'

This was a very foolish thing for Hannelore Hommerich to say and it clearly demonstrated that she had no understanding of modern young people and their problems. The dreaded generation gap had reared whatever passes for a head in a gap.

'I'll take it up with the board,' said Thorsten, and he did.

212

The Three Musketeers listened as attentively as anyone under the influence of narcotics can listen.

'As I have already told you many times,' said Wuschl, 'we are, unfortunately, going to have to waste Mama. If I don't stop dealing, she's going to blow the whistle on us.'

'We?' said Heiko. 'It's your mother.'

'All right. Me then,' said Wuschl, accepting responsibility with the courage of the born leader. 'You can still suggest something.'

'Get the first one straight in through the heart,' recommended Sabine. 'Then she won't squeak so much.'

'No cutting,' said Heiko. 'I can't stand the sight of blood.'

'Make it look like suicide,' said Andreas. 'You could throw her off the balcony.'

'Nobody commits suicide jumping off a first-floor balcony,' said Wuschl.

'An accident then,' said Heiko. 'She was drunk and she fell off the balcony.'

'Onto the lawn and sprained her ankle,' scoffed Wuschl. 'You're all worse than useless. I'll have to think of something myself.'

And, on the late afternoon of 20 October 1983, he did.

The four good friends were sitting in Wuschl's old room in his mother's house listening to rock records and rolling joints.

Hannelore Hommerich was in the kitchen baking cookies for her son and his friends.

She had just taken them out of the oven and gone into the living room when Wuschl got purposefully to his feet, went to the kitchen, came out immediately and went into the bathroom.

'Mama?' he called. 'Come here a minute. There's some kind of an animal in the bathtub.'

In Wuschl's old room down the hall, the Three

Musketeers exchanged thrilled glances. They did not think there was an animal in the bathtub.

Neither did Hannelore, but her son was calling her and she went.

'See?' said Wuschl, pointing into the tub.

Hannelore bent over the tub and her son plunged the ten-inch serrated blade of the family bread knife, which he had concealed inside his shirt, into her back with all his force.

The knife was sharp and, unlike most bread knives, had a sharp point. As the autopsy would later show, the blade penetrated for a depth of nearly eight inches, slicing into the pancreas, perforating the left lung and severing a number of important blood vessels.

For Hannelore, this was excruciatingly painful and she screamed terrifyingly, the shrill, throat-tearing scream of the human female in fear of death.

In Wuschl's room down the hall, the Three Musketeers moved instinctively closer together and Heiko turned up the volume of the record player, already operating at an ear-splitting level.

In the bathroom, Hannelore had swung about to face the son who was murdering her and was fighting for her life.

And as she fought, she pleaded. 'No, Torry!' calling him by his little boy's name. 'Don't do it! You'll go to prison, Torry. Don't hurt me! I'm your mother!'

But Torry was ten years gone and this was Wuschl, the successful businessman with an investment to protect. He jerked the knife out of her back and he stabbed and slashed at her stomach, her belly and her breasts, the same breasts from which he had once fed.

Hannelore continued to plead and to fight. 'No, Torry! Oh God! It hurts so! Stop, Torry! You're killing me!'

She was in superb physical condition as a result of the aerobic dancing and this was unfortunate for it took her a long time to die.

Precisely how long was never ascertained for none of

the participants was able to say with certainty when Wuschl had called his mother into the bathroom. It was, however, a little after nine-thirty when he appeared in the doorway of the bedroom, covered from head to foot with blood.

'Get these clothes off me,' he ordered.

The sounds from the bathroom had ceased. Under the violence of the blows, the bread knife had snapped in half and Wuschl had been forced to finish the job with the handleless blade gripped in his fingers, a dangerous operation as he could have cut himself painfully.

He had not, however, and his friends quickly stripped off his blood-soaked clothing and packed it into plastic grocery sacks.

Wuschl washed and got into fresh clothing and Sabine came to hold him tight and kiss him for close to half an hour. As she later said, he was in need of comfort at such a moment for the murder had upset him terribly and he kept saying, 'How awful! She made such a noise! And she took such a time about it.'

Heiko and Andreas were less concerned with Wuschl's emotions and more concerned with their own skins. Their drug-damaged minds were not always able to distinguish between imagination and reality and they had not grasped that Wuschl was really going to murder his mother until he was doing so.

Now, they not only realized that the murder had taken place, but that they were accessories to it. As they knew nothing about the German legal system, they believed they could be punished and it made them nervous.

'We'll have to make it look like somebody broke in and killed her,' said Heiko. 'Can you make it look like that, Wuschl?'

Wuschl could. Returning to the bathroom, he dragged his mother's still-warm corpse over the edge of the tub, pulled up her house-coat and ripped away her panties, getting his hands bloody again in the process.

He then picked up the handle of the knife from the

floor, pulled the blade out of Hannelore's rib-cage and returned to the room where the friends were waiting.

'We'll have to get rid of the knife and clothes,' he said. 'Maybe we can throw them in the Lenne.'

The Lenne river, a not very large steam, runs through Attendorn.

'Not here,' said Andreas. 'We'll throw the knife in the river at Lennestadt. It's deep under the bridge there.'

'And we can burn the clothes in the old quarry on the Lennestadt road,' added Heiko. Both he and Andreas were more mentally alert than they had been for years.

In Andreas' car, they drove silently to Lennestadt. The rays of the rising moon glinted briefly on the blade of the knife as it arced downward to the black waters beneath the bridge. Although the near-full moon was yellow, the reflection seemed strangely red.

It was approaching midnight when the pile of sticks soaked with petrol from the car's reserve cannister flared brightly beneath the bloody clothing in the old quarry, the garish light throwing grotesque, monstrous shadows along the vertical stone walls.

The young people were excited, exhilarated even. It was like the films or television. A tight little group of the best of friends united against the world. In a dull universe, something had finally happened in Attendorn.

But then the moon went in behind a cloud and the fire died down and it was dark and cold in the old quarry. The rising wind whistling through the crevices of the rock walls sounded almost like the voice of a woman, pleading, beseeching, 'Don't do it, Torry! You'll go to jail!'

Naturally, no mother wanted her boy to go to jail and Wuschl was determined to respect his mother's last wish. Getting back into the car, the four friends drove to Attendorn, where Wuschl got out in front of the police station while the others continued on to the apartment in Lenhausen.

At exactly seven minutes past midnight, according

to the police blotter, Thorsten Hommerich entered the charge room of the Attendorn police station and advanced to the desk.

The duty officer looked up from the magazine he was reading. 'Yes?' he said.

'My name is Thorsten Hommerich,' said Wuschl. 'I have just come from my mother's house at Hellepaedchen 32. It looks to me as if she's been murdered.'

The report caused the desk sergeant to drop his magazine and knock over the little tub of pencils and other equipment on the desk.

It was thirty-four years since there had been a homicide in Attendorn. Not a single member of the force at that time was still on active duty.

For an instant, the thought crossed the sergeant's mind that the caller must be drunk, but Thorsten did not look drunk. He was, as a matter of fact, cleaner, neater and more suitably dressed than he had been for years. Drugs did not occur to the sergeant. Like the other members of the police, he did not think that there was a drug problem in Attendorn.

Wuschl was waiting patiently and politely and the sergeant summoned his two duty constables, who were playing cards in the squad room, and told them to accompany Thorsten to the address and report back immediately on what they found.

A short time later, he received an almost hysterical report over the radio telephone. An ambulance was needed. The coroner was needed. The homicide squad was needed. This was murder, bloody murder!

The ambulance was sent and the coroner was pulled out of bed, but the homicide squad was not alerted because there was no homicide squad. With the last homicide thirty-four years back, one was scarcely needed.

The homicide squad, therefore, came up from Olpe and consisted initially of Inspector Ludwig Kranzer, Detective Sergeant Peter Berg and a medical expert named Alfred Dingermann. All had, of course, been in bed at the time that the call was received.

Arriving at the scene, the investigators found present an ambulance and crew, the Attendorn coroner and very nearly the entire Attendorn police force. Thorsten was not present. He had asked to be excused and gone back to Lenhausen. He was tired and he found the death of his mother very upsetting, he said.

The police found it, if anything, more so. Although the Olpe homicide unit had greater experience in such matters as they were responsible for the entire district, it was their first encounter with such a savage and apparently sexually motivated murder as this.

The sergeant and half a dozen members of the Attendorn police had gone through the house and found that money and jewellery were lying about exposed and had not been touched. Dr Dingermann, who had been examining the corpse in the meantime, reported that sex did not appear to have been the motive either.

'A rather clumsy attempt to fake a sex crime,' said the doctor, who was short, plump, blond and often struck women as cuddly. 'The indications are that she was already dead when she was draped over the edge of the bathtub and her clothing torn away. There's no trace of semen in or on the sex organs and no apparent attempt at penetration. She's been dead for three or four hours. Multiple stab wounds and fatal haemorrhaging. Remarkably good physical condition for her age. She must be in her fifties. Any idea who she was?'

The Attendorn police had a formal identification by the victim's son and, in any case, Hannelore's face was not marked and there were a number of pictures of her in the house, including one in her personal identity card.

Identification of the victim was, therefore, no problem, but identification of the murderer was.

As the first suspect in the murder of a married person is automatically the spouse, Inspector Kranzer, a comparatively young man with stylish sideburns and a near-classic profile, began by taking into custody Papa Hommerich, who, although no longer married to the victim, might have harboured ill feeling against her.

Papa Hommerich swore that he did not, but he was not arrested until the twenty-fourth, the day of his ex-wife's funeral and, by that time he was not completely certain where he had been or what he had been doing with whom on the afternoon and evening of the twentieth. Papa was still living the full life with more mistresses than ever, and his schedule was complex.

Eventually, however, he was able to recall his activities on the day in question and to provide enough evidence of the accuracy of his statements that he was released, although not removed entirely from the suspect list.

As a matter of fact, he was the only person on the list at the moment. No one suspected Wuschl because no one knew of any possible motive for the young man to murder his mother.

The outline of a motive only began to appear when Wuschl was, more or less routinely, included in the background studies of all persons close to the victim.

The investigators were intrigued by the fact that Wuschl appeared to enjoy an extremely affluent lifestyle (with the exception of household furnishings), but had no visible source of income.

Having had a look at Miss Ahrens, Sergeant Berg, a pleasant-appearing soul with a round, bland, pink-and-white face, came to the conclusion that Wuschl's income derived from the leasing of Miss Ahrens' anatomy, but the Attendorn police said no. There were teenage prostitutes in Attendorn, but Sabine was not one of them.

'Fascinating,' said the inspector. 'Well, the money's got to come from somewhere. Find out where.'

The sergeant found out and, actually, when he applied himself to it, it was not very hard. Wuschl was the sole dealer for the area and the traffic through the apartment in Lenhausen was roughly equivalent to that of a medium-size department store. It was noticeable.

And the customers were vulnerable. A few days in detention and they began to experience withdrawal symptoms, at which time they were willing and eager to tell the investigators anything they knew or even things they did not know in return for being allowed access to their favoured narcotic.

'This enterprising youth has the drug business sewn up for the whole area,' said the sergeant. 'He killed his mother because she was going to squeal on him or because she wanted a cut.'

'I don't believe it,' said the inspector. 'A fine young man like that? Good God! This isn't Berlin or Munich.'

The final statement was correct. It was not Berlin or Munich, but the fine young man had, indeed, killed his mother and, when the inspector talked to the police officers who had been in contact with him on the night of the crime, he too became convinced.

Wuschl, it seemed, had been cool, much, much too cool. Whatever excitement he had felt at the time of the murder had been comforted away by his friends and he had reported his mother's death with all the emotion of a spectator at a turtle race. The Attendorn officers had been so excited themselves that they had not been impressed by Wuschl's casual manner at the time, but they remembered it later.

Taken into custody, Wuschl, at first, stoutly denied all knowledge of his mother's death, but the Three Musketeers' principle of All for One and One for All did not bear up well in this case and D'Artagnan was roundly denounced by his companions, who strove heroically to load all of the blame on to him while whitewashing themselves.

Saddened by this lack of solidarity, Wuschl too broke down and filled in whatever details his friends had left out.

Some might fear that these sensitive, if somewhat misguided, young persons could have their lives ruined through harsh prison sentences, but only those who did not understand the German legal system.

Although, with the exception of Sabine, the participants were legally adults with all of the rights and privileges of such, in one respect and one respect only, they were children. Under the German juvenile code, the maximum sentence any of them could receive was ten years' imprisonment, and that was what they did receive on 16 November 1984.

It is very unusual that a juvenile receiving a ten-year sentence actually serves more than four years of it.

Who was the deviate? The dynamic, enterprising Wuschl?

How so? The man was in business. There was a lot of money involved. Was he to give it up because Mummy said so? After all, she wanted him to acquire a profession, and what could be more modern and progressive than pushing?

The Three Musketeers?

Hardly. They were really only spectators, or rather auditors, as they were to everything else in their lives.

Well, who then?

What about Hannelore Hommerich?

Germany is a democracy. She must have helped elect to office those who enact laws making it possible to kill your mother and suffer no more than minor inconvenience for it.

That should be deviate behaviour enough for our purposes.

16

A HAIRY TALE

From Lichtenau to Kassel is only about thirty-five miles. Both communities lie in the West German state of Hessen. Kassel is, however, a city of over two hundred thousand inhabitants and Lichtenau is a tiny village which barely appears on the map.

On 29 May 1981, a nineteen-year-old girl with a fine mane of long blonde hair set out to hitch-hike from Lichtenau to Kassel. She never made it.

Hessen is roughly in the centre of West Germany and not all May mornings are pleasant, but this one was. The sun shone golden yellow. Trees, bushes, grass, flowers, all were in leaf or in bloom and by ten o'clock the temperature was touching eighty degrees Fahrenheit.

Heike Freiheit left the home of her uncle in Lichtenau in high spirits. A pretty, good-natured girl, she did not have a great many problems. Her last name means freedom in German and she was worthy of it.

Heike's father had died in 1978 and, as her mother had left the family a good deal earlier, she had moved in with her father's brother, who kept a rather absent eye on her. He did not feel himself adequate to coping with a nineteen-year-old totally liberated female, but then, there are few who would.

In any case, Heike came and went more or less as she saw fit and it was, therefore, over a month before her uncle began to wonder what had happened to her. She was not an aggressively liberated girl and she usually let him know where she was, if not what she was doing.

This time, apparently not. The uncle did not know what to do. He had no idea of where she was planning to stay in Kassel, who she knew there or why she had wanted to go there in the first place. After a great deal of hesitation, he telephoned the Kassel police long-distance and asked if they could look for Heike.

The Kassel police replied that they would be happy to do so. One entire department of the police was devoted solely to looking for missing persons and, at the moment, there were around six hundred active cases, most of them young girls.

This did not sound very promising and it was not. The Kassel police did look for Heike, but they never found any trace of her at all, at all.

For a good reason, of course. Heike never made it to Kassel.

Now, the town of Padborg is a long way north of both Kassel and Lichtenau, such a long way, in fact, that it is not even in Germany, but just over the border in Denmark.

On 25 September 1981, six months after Heike Freiheit had set out for Kassel, the Padborg police made a descent upon a none-too-attractive apartment house located at 18 Jernbanegade, where they carried out a rather desultory search of an attic apartment occupied by twenty-nine-year-old Luigi Richard Longhi.

The police thought that Mr Longhi had stolen something, but, if he had, they did not find it and withdrew hurriedly as the apartment did not smell very good.

Even though they had found nothing in the small, untidy apartment where the ceiling sloped down to low partitions beneath the eaves, the police still regarded Longhi with a certain amount of suspicion. He was not only a foreigner, but a confusing sort of one.

Born in Switzerland, an occurrence which did not, however, confer Swiss nationality upon him, Longhi was of Italian descent and was legally a national of Italy.

From what the police knew about him, he had lived almost everywhere but Italy.

In 1977, he had been expelled from Switzerland for unknown reasons and lived for a time in Germany, where he held a number of unskilled jobs in the town of Neustadt an der Weinstrasse, which means merely New City on the Wine Road.

In 1979, he had come to Denmark, where he found a job in a saw mill at the town of Holbi. A year later he moved to Padborg, where he was currently employed as a filling-station attendant.

Why the police found Longhi suspicious was never explained. He had no police record in either Germany or Denmark and, if he had one in Switzerland, the Swiss were not prepared to discuss it. Possibly, it was simply because he was an obvious southern European and there are few from the sunny Mediterranean who live without extremely pressing reasons in such a frozen and freezing place as the Danish-German border.

In any case, they did not search his apartment nearly as thoroughly as they should have. All that they could find wrong with Luigi Richard Longhi was that he stank, which is not a chargeable offence in Denmark.

The other occupants of the apartment house were inclined to wish that it was. For months they had been complaining to the owner that the building stank abominably, but, as he did not live there himself, he regarded the complaints as typical tenant carping, possibly initiated in the hope of obtaining a reduction in the rent.

'I don't smell anything,' he said, standing in the front hall and holding his breath. 'It's your imagination.'

Water coming through the roof could not, however, be imagination and quite a bit having come through during that winter of 1981–82, the landlord engaged a roofing firm to come as soon as the weather permitted and effect repairs.

The roofing company workers arrived on Monday, 29 March 1982 and began tearing off the tiles of the old

224

roof. The landlord would later complain that this was not necessary, but, fortunately, he did not know what was going on until a good part of the roof was already off.

One of the people actually pulling off those old tiles was a young Dane named Sven Jorgensen. He was an unskilled labourer, as no particular skill is needed for pulling off old tiles.

Good lungs were, however, and Jorgensen soon found himself nearly asphyxiated by the most vile stench he had ever encountered in his life, even though he was working out in the open air.

Because of the manner in which tiles are laid, it was necessary for Jorgensen to begin at the peak of the roof and work downward toward the eaves, and the closer he came to them, the worse the smell.

Removing a row of tiles a scant three feet from the edge of the roof, Jorgensen found himself gazing down into the space behind the partitions forming the walls of Luigi Richard Longhi's attic apartment.

It was a sunny day and he could see clearly between the slats which supported the tiles. There was something lying in the space, something long, strangely formed . . .

Jorgensen held his breath, put his head down, looked closer, gave a yell of horror and fell off the roof.

What he had seen was a sort of surrealist sculpture, a weirdly formed mass of a whitish-grey substance with a white powder covering everything, and projecting from this strange cocoon one skeletal hand and forearm and a grinning, nearly fleshless skull topped grotesquely by a great mane of long blonde hair.

Sven Jorgensen had accomplished what the Kassel police could not. He had found Heike Freiheit.

As he had never met her previously, he did not, of course, recognize her, but, even had he been her mother, he would have had difficulty in doing that.

'It would be even worse,' said Dr Olaf Sorensen, 'if she hadn't been sprinkled with lime.'

The doctor, tall, lean, black-haired and slightly awkward-looking, had just completed the on-the-spot examination of the body and crawled gratefully back out of the hole which the inspector and sergeant had made in the partition.

They, like the doctor, had come down from Abenra, twenty-five miles to the north, which, although a community of scarcely more than twenty thousand inhabitants, was the administrative centre for all of South Jutland.

Being sturdily built and lucky, Sven Jorgensen had not broken anything in his fall from the roof. He had run straight to the Padborg police, who investigated and promptly summoned the homicide squad in Abenra.

But not before taking into custody Luigi Richard Longhi at his place of work. They had not questioned him or even informed him why he was being arrested, and he was now sitting in the detention cell normally reserved for drunks at the Padborg police station.

As he had neither protested nor asked any questions, it seemed probable that he had a good idea of the reasons for his arrest.

And, indeed, he had. Confronted with the fact that the corpse of a girl had been found behind the partition of his apartment, he immediately admitted that he had put her there. The police had not needed to make a hole in the partition. One of the panels was removable.

Longhi said that he had put the girl there because she was dead and he had not known what else to do with her.

He had tried to cause as little trouble as possible and, when the other tenants of the building began complaining about the smell, he bought some containers of plastic foam and what he thought was a bag of cement. With this, he proposed to completely envelope the corpse and make it, more or less, a part of the building.

The plan had not worked out very well. The supposed cement turned out to be lime and the plastic foam was

226

not adequate to entirely cover the body. He spread the lime over it anyway and withdrew. It had been, he said, very unpleasant working in the small space under the eaves with the corpse which was, by this time, more than half rotten.

'I'm sure,' said Inspector Karl Andersen, who was large, blond and looked the way that most people think Danes should look, 'but who was she and why did you do it?'

Like everyone else, the inspector assumed that the victim was Danish, but Longhi said, no, she was German or, at least, she had spoken German like a German.

Otherwise, he knew little about her. Her first name was Heike and he had met her in a small café near the railway station on the evening of 30 May 1981. She said that she was looking for a place to spend the night and he suggested his apartment. She accepted.

Up to this point, Longhi was cooperative and even appeared to be prepared to confess to the murder of the girl, but on the subject of what had actually happened at the apartment, he was much more reticent, saying merely that there had been an unfortunate misunderstanding.

The inspector thought that the misunderstanding had probably been of a sexual nature. Longhi would logically have assumed that, if the girl accepted an invitation to spend the night at his apartment, she was prepared to spend it with him in bed. It was possible that Heike had had different ideas.

Living so close to the border, the inspector had had some experience with liberated West German girls and he was aware that some, at least, would regard the exchange of sex for lodging as a violation of the principles of equality of the sexes. Sexual contacts were only permissible by mutual agreement, not subject to compensation and, ideally, in connection with a meaningful relationship.

Such a sophisticated philosophy might have been

difficult to explain to a sexually aroused filling-station attendant.

What happened then, the inspector surmised, was that Longhi had taken or attempted to take by force what he could not obtain by consent, and he had ended up strangling the girl.

According to the autopsy, that was exactly what he had done. Heike had been strangled with a thin cord, which was still around the place where her neck had been.

She had also been bound and gagged at the time, for the bonds and the gag were found in the plastic foam covering a part of the body.

Whether she had been raped or not could no longer be ascertained. Nothing remained of Heike's sex organs at all.

Nor much of the rest of her, with the exception of the long blonde hair. Dr Sorensen was able, however, to make a fairly accurate estimate of her height, weight and general build, and to determine that she had while yet a child broken one of the bones in her left foot and that this had been put right by a doctor.

The information from the autopsy, the date of the disappearance, the presumed nationality and the name of Heike were, perhaps, enough to effect an identification and the details were sent off to the West German authorities with an account of the circumstances of the crime and a request for any information that could be obtained concerning Luigi Richard Longhi during his sojourn in West Germany.

To the inspector's surprise, the response was quick.

Within less than a week, an answer was received from the national identification centre in Wiesbaden to the effect that the victim was possibly Heike Freiheit, reported missing in the Kassel area around the end of May 1981 and that, if Longhi had done anything illegal in Neustadt an der Weinstrasse, the police had not known of it. A search of the records of unsolved cases of missing or murdered females in the region for the period in question was being undertaken.

The inspector's case was, therefore, largely complete. There was a tentative identification of the victim, which would later be confirmed from Heike's medical records – she had broken a bone in her foot as a child – and there was an excellent suspect in the form of Luigi Richard Longhi, behind the partition of whose apartment the body had been found.

'He hasn't actually confessed to the murder,' said Sergeant of Detectives Baldur Kracken, the inspector's second in command of the Abenra homicide squad, who did not like to see his chief looking quite so smug.

'He will,' said the inspector confidently. 'What choice does he have? The body was behind the partition of his room and he admits he put it there.'

'But he only says that there was an unfortunate misunderstanding,' said the sergeant. 'I wonder what he'll testify in court and what the defence will make out of it.'

Although the sergeant had a very Scandinavian name, he was relatively short, with the brown hair, brown eyes and olive complexion of southern Europe.

The inspector looked slightly uneasy. There was something in what the sergeant said. Going to court with no clear idea of what the accused was going to testify was risky.

'You suggest?' he said.

'He was kicked out of Switzerland,' said the sergeant. 'He must have done something. This being a homicide case, the Swiss should cooperate and, if we know what he did there, it may throw light on what happened here. There's no evidence that it was a sex crime. We don't really have a motive.'

'True, true,' mused the inspector. 'I don't know about the Swiss. From what I've heard, they don't need a reason to throw you out of the country. Still, we can try.'

*

Before trying the Swiss, however, the inspector called in a psychologist to carry out an examination of Longhi, now formally indicted on an undefined homicide charge and bound over for trial. The psychologist was to attempt to get more information from Longhi concerning his motives for the murder than the police had succeeded in doing so far.

The psychologist spent a few weeks at this task, but was unable to penetrate Longhi's reserve.

'It's not that he's uncooperative,' he reported. 'It's that he's ashamed. There's something about women's hair that's connected with his mother and he won't or can't talk about it. He says he's going to plead guilty at the trial so that he won't have to explain anything.'

'So he says,' said the sergeant sceptically.

'You have a suspicious nature, Baldur,' said the inspector. 'Well, I suppose it's the Swiss.'

Contrary to expectations, there was no problem with the Swiss police nor, it seemed, had they been so brusque in their treatment of Longhi as had been believed.

The fact was, Longhi had not been too desirable a citizen by any country's standards. Born to a somewhat carefree mother, he landed in an orphanage at the age of two, where he remained until the age of nine. Then his mother decided to resume her responsibilities and took him to live with her.

Longhi stayed with his mother until the age of seventeen, at which time he was arrested on a curious charge. He had, according to police and court records, waited for a young female hairdresser to come out from work, threatened her with a knife and, having taken her to her own room, washed her hair against her will.

Longhi had done nothing else to the girl and the police were, for a time, at a loss as to what the charge should be. It had not occurred to the law-makers to provide an appropriate punishment for forced hair washes.

In the end, he was charged with threats with a deadly weapon and put on two years' probation. He had been more frank with the Swiss psychologists than with the one in Abenra and they came to the conclusion that he was not dangerous, in spite of the knife.

Longhi, it seemed, not having lived with his mother from the age of two to nine, did not regard her in an entirely filial manner. Although there was no suggestion of an incestuous relationship, he developed the habit of masturbating into her wig, which was long and blonde and to which he applied liberal amounts of shampoo for the purpose. She was, of course, neither wearing it nor present at the time.

Unfortunately, this comparatively harmless perversion soon turned into a less harmless one. Longhi could no longer obtain sexual satisfaction with his mother's wig. He required the hair of a living woman, and it had to be long and blonde.

There was also another difference. Longhi did not now masturbate directly into the hair, but achieved orgasm through simply applying shampoo and washing it.

The act put him into such a state that he was able to arrive at a climax three and more times in succession, the intervals between ejaculations becoming, understandably, increasingly longer so that the process took up the best part of an evening.

As Longhi showed no tendency to sadism or violence and as he was literally incapable of raping his victims in the conventional manner, the psychologists recommended treatment and probation rather than a prison sentence.

Longhi did not, however, respond to treatment. Less than a year later, he abducted a young physical therapist and subjected her to no less than six hours of continuous hair washing, an experience which left both exhausted.

This time the matter was more serious. Longhi had, once again, threatened the victim with a knife. Worse, he had also bound and gagged her and he had placed a noose around her neck, although he had not drawn it tight.

Despite this second offence and a less favourable opinion by the psychologists, Longhi was still allowed his freedom, but under closer surveillance.

This did not prevent him from washing several more young ladies' hair and, in 1977, the Swiss finally became impatient and put him out of the country. The reasons for his expulsion were not given, presumably because it would have made it difficult to find a country that would accept him.

From that date up to the time of his arrest in Padborg, Longhi had had no police record of any kind, either in Germany or in Denmark.

The inspector did not think that this meant he had given up washing girls' hair. He thought that he had simply become more clever about it.

'Giving up washing women's hair would be for him the equivalent of giving up sex altogether,' he said. 'There's nothing in the record that says he had to do it against their will. He probably just started paying them.'

'Undoubtedly,' agreed the sergeant, 'but, if so, why did he murder Heike Freiheit? A disagreement over the price? He said there was a misunderstanding.'

'There's only one person who can answer that,' said the inspector, 'and I think that once he realizes that we know all about his sex problems, he will.'

Luigi Richard Longhi would. He did not like being a pervert and he had no intention of evading responsibility for what he had done, but he had been reluctant to discuss his motives or his actions in the attic apartment as they appeared bizarre even to him.

He was, he said, cursed with a strange sickness. There was no way in the world that he could obtain sexual satisfaction other than through washing the long blonde hair of a girl. He had tried everything and nothing worked.

The girl did not have to resist. The process worked equally well if she was consenting, and he had managed well with prostitutes while he was in Germany.

232

On other occasions, he had picked up young girls and had simply asked them to let him wash their hair. Many had not objected.

One such pick-up had, however, turned out badly when the girl wanted intercourse and became abusive when she discovered that he was incapable of it. She threatened to go to the police and say that he had raped her and, as she was only fourteen years old, he became frightened and left Germany to come to Denmark.

The situation in Denmark was worse. Holbi was very small and there were no prostitutes at all. He had, therefore, moved to Padborg, where there were a few, but, by mischance, it turned out that none of them were blonde except one, and she wore her hair short.

He was badly frustrated sexually when he encountered Heike in the café, and he asked her almost point-blank whether she would mind him giving her a shampoo.

Heike, who was a good-natured girl and far from prudish, undoubtedly believed that she would end up with more than a hair wash and, as Longhi was not physically unattractive by the undemanding standards of modern youth, she agreed.

He had not even felt it necessary to tie and gag her at first, but, after the fourth hair wash, Heike became restless and he tied her up and gagged her as he was afraid that she would make enough noise to alarm the other tenants.

'The fourth?' said the inspector.

'Well, yes,' said Longhi modestly looking down at the floor. It had been a long time, he added apologetically.

'Continue,' said the inspector.

Heike became, said Longhi, not frightened, but angry and, as her feet were not tied, she began to stamp violently on the floor.

In order to stop her, he drew tight the noose that he had put around her neck and the next thing he knew, she was dead. It had been as simple as that.

'You continued to wash her hair after she was dead?' asked the inspector.

Longhi shook his head sadly. 'No,' he said, 'It has to be a live girl for me.'

On 11 February 1983, a jury in the nearby town of Sonderborg listened to Luigi Richard Longhi's account of the crime, heard his admission that he had previously shampooed the hair of twelve other more or less consenting maidens, making Heike the unlucky thirteenth, and tried to decide what was to be done with him.

It was obvious that he had not killed with premeditation or even with intent. Heike's death actually put an end to the only use that he had for her.

It was also obvious that he regretted very bitterly his act.

However, that did not alter the fact that he was potentially dangerous and could most certainly be expected to resume his hair-washing activities once the sexual pressure became too strong for him to resist.

In the end, the court found him guilty of unpremeditated murder and sentenced him to life, but not in prison. Sent to a closed institution for sex psychopaths, he was to benefit from a review of his case if it was believed that he had responded to treatment.

17

ARTISTS AND MODELS

Not all dogs in West Germany are named Waldi, but a great many are, and on the evening of 30 June 1978 a dachshund with a slightly dubious pedigree who bore this name was taking his associate for a walk in the fields near the village of Kirkel-Altstadt.

The walk was progressing a little too slowly for Waldi's taste. The associate, who preferred to think of himself as master, was forty-one years old and rather given to the pleasures of the table. He was not, therefore, as enthusiastic about running into all the ditches, snuffling through all the thickets and racing wildly down the field paths as was Waldi.

Even so, both Karl Bauer and his dog looked forward to their late-afternoon walks and this was a particularly fine one.

The summer solstice was only a week past and, at eight o'clock, it was still broad daylight. The weather was excellent and the entire countryside was in leaf and bloom. Although the great highway leading from the city of Saarbruecken on the German-French border to the town of Neunkirchen was not far away, the sound of the endless stream of vehicles passing over it did not reach this far and the tree-lined fields were quiet, fragrant and peaceful.

Except, of course, for the barking of stupid, far too exuberant dogs.

'Shut up, Waldi!' yelled Bauer, pounding with his walking stick on the ground. 'Shut up this minute!'

But Waldi would not shut up, which did not surprise Bauer very much. The little dachshund had many virtues, but obedience was not among them.

What did surprise Bauer was that the dog was standing still and barking. Barks were usually brought on by wild chases after real or imaginary rabbits, but now Waldi was standing rigidly alert and barking at what looked like a partially burned log.

As Bauer drew nearer, he saw the explanation for Waldi's concern. The log was apparently still burning, for thin trails of smoke were rising from it.

Conscious of the danger of fire in a wooded area such as this, Bauer hurried forward to stamp out the sparks.

The log moved!

And spoke! Or tried to speak. The sounds that rasped from the throat were barely human, a low, weak, keening sound, crying out a suffering beyond expression.

Rooted to the spot, Bauer stood staring down at a sight that burned itself so indelibly into his brain that he would never forget it, although he would have given anything in the world to be able to.

What lay there on the scorched grass was the body of a woman. There was no question of that, for her clothing had been burned entirely away. Whether she had been old or young, beautiful or ugly, blonde or brunette was impossible to say, for her hair had vanished and her skin was no more than a blackened crust, cracking and bursting in places to display the angry red, blood-oozing flesh beneath.

It seemed impossible that any human being could be burned in such a manner and remain alive.

This human was not only alive but conscious and, as Bauer later admitted, his first instinct was to kill her. The sight of such suffering was too much to bear. Death would be a release.

Bauer was, however, no killer and, like many Germans of his generation, he was public-spirited and he had faith in the authorities. It was up to them to do something.

236

At a pace of which he would not have believed himself capable, Bauer ran headlong in the direction of the village and a telephone.

Kirkel-Altstadt is too small to have much in the way of emergency services, but Saarbruecken is a scant seven miles away and it has a population of close to a quarter of a million.

Bauer did not, therefore, seek help in Kirkel-Altstadt, but telephoned directly the Saarbruecken emergency service, stammering out such a graphic and horrifying description of what he had found that a rescue helicopter took off immediately. Eight minutes later it set down at the point where Bauer was standing waving his cane with his handkerchief tied to the end of it.

He had not managed to make it all the way back to the woman and he was so out of breath from running that he could only point in the right direction. As his family doctor would later say, he only escaped by a whisker becoming a victim himself.

The stretcher-bearers from the helicopter set off on a run and, within minutes, the hideously burned woman, still conscious as the paramedic had not dared to give her an injection, was on her way to a hospital that specialized in the treatment of massive burns.

This hospital, one of the finest in Germany, was equipped with the most modern technology known to medical science. Miracles had taken place there, but there would be no miracle this time.

At ten-thirty in the evening of 1 July 1978, Carmen Cojaniz, who had been born Carmen Aeschlimann, drew her last agonized breath. She had retained consciousness up to the very end, although she was drowsy from the massive injections of pain-killers which she had received.

Carmen had fought to remain conscious because she too was public-spirited and she was afraid that what had happened to her could happen to another woman unless the madman responsible was rendered harmless.

Who this madman was, she could not say, for she

had never seen him before in her life until that Friday afternoon when she was waiting to cross the street at a traffic light on the corner of Eschberger Way in Saarbruecken.

The man, who was driving a grey Opel Ascona with a Saarbruecken licence plate, passed her, returned and passed her again three or four times.

Carmen was not unduly alarmed. She was used to such interest. An outstandingly beautiful woman with a magnificent figure, she was her husband's favourite model and her perfectly formed breasts appeared in nearly every picture he had ever painted since their meeting on the Spanish Costa Brava in 1966.

Carmen was Swiss and came from the city of Basel. Norbert Cojaniz was a professional artist and came from Duesseldorf. Both were on holiday and both fell head-over-heels in love at first sight. They married a month later.

And lived happily ever after, for twelve years at least. Norbert was successful with his painting, due, he swore, largely to the beauty of his subject, and Carmen was happy in her role of wife and model. They did not yet have any children for fear of the effect that it might have on Carmen's figure.

Carmen did not immediately tell the doctors about Norbert. She was anxious to provide a description of the man who had burned her before she died. It was utterly vital that he be caught for, otherwise, perhaps one day another woman or girl would be standing beside the street waiting to cross and the Opel Ascona would pull in to the kerb and the man would point the dangerous-looking pistol and order, 'Get in!'

And then it would be too late. The man would drive out towards Neunkirchen and force the girl to strip herself totally naked, and then he would kiss her.

Karl Bauer was mistaken. Carmen's clothing had not been burned away. She was naked when she was set on fire.

238

But not raped. The only intimacy was that single kiss. The man then drove to the field path near Kirkel-Altstadt, where he took a nylon rope from the trunk of the Opel and bound her hand and foot.

Carrying her some twenty or thirty feet from the car, he laid her on the grass and returned to the car to fetch a standard reserve cannister of petrol such as many motorists carried for emergencies.

Nearly insane with fear, Carmen felt him pour the cold petrol over her from head to foot, and then there was an unbearable short wait while he returned once again to the car.

She dared not think what he had gone for, but it was, of course, matches. She saw the deadly little flame spring up as he struck the match and then there was the sudden whoosh of burning petrol, black smoke before her eyes, an unbelievable sensation of heat and agony beyond description.

How long the agony went on or whether the man had stayed to gloat over her sufferings, she could not say. It was about six o'clock in the afternoon when she was forced into the car and she supposed that it was around six-thirty when she was set on fire. After that, she no longer had any clear concept of time or her surroundings. There was only the pain, the terrible, all-encompassing pain. Even now, despite the injections, she could feel it. It would never leave her.

The man, said Carmen Cojaniz, her cooked lips cracking from the movement in forming words, was young, not yet thirty. He had dark hair and brown eyes and comparatively regular features. He was five feet eight or nine inches tall and muscular. There was a black mole or birthmark the size of a small coin beneath his left ear at the point of the jaw. There was a larger, similar birthmark on the back of his left hand. He was clean-shaven and had a short, conventional haircut. His fingernails were rimmed with black as if he had washed his hands carefully but had not been able to get all of the dirt out from under the nails. He was wearing grey summer trousers with a broad belt, the buckle of which was of yellow metal like brass and in the shape of a lion's head. He had on a short-sleeved, pale-green sports shirt, open at the neck, and moccasin-type brown shoes. He smelled of shaving lotion, but she did not know what kind.

Having done all that she could to bring to justice the man who had murdered her, Carmen asked to see Norbert as she thought she was going to die very soon.

It was not as soon as she expected, but, when she was finally released from her suffering, it was with Norbert holding her blackened, mutilated hands while the tears streamed down his cheeks in an agony nearly as unbearable as hers.

The love story was over.

And so too was the detective story. Even before his victim was dead, one of the most cruel and inexcusable murderers in the annals of the German police had been taken into custody and was pouring out a self-pitying justification for a crime that could never be justified.

Carmen's description of what had taken place and her descriptions of the murderer, his clothing and his car were taken down on a tape recorder and the latter part of the statement was heard personally by Inspector Morris Belder and Detective Sergeant Leopold Freimann, both of the Saarbruecken police homicide squad.

Although it did not occur to Karl Bauer to summon the police, the pilot of the emergency helicopter had immediately realized that the burning was a criminal act and contacted police headquarters over the helicopter's radio while the craft was still in the air.

The pilot expressed the opinion that the victim's injuries would prove to be fatal and the homicide squad was, therefore, called away at the double, racing through the streets with the siren of the police car wide open, to

240

the hospital in the hope of obtaining a statement from the victim before she died.

In this they were more successful than they expected. Carmen's description of the murderer was so precise the police artist would be able to prepare such an accurate drawing that even persons who did not know him could recognize him from it instantly.

The homicide squad officers brought with them a police medical expert. He was, however, unable to do anything at the hospital and could only report that death had been the result of massive burns covering the entire body when he performed the obligatory autopsy the following day.

Inspector Belder, a hatchet-faced man with a lean, hard body and very short-cut sandy-red hair, had been able to do more.

He had rushed the description of the killer to police headquarters, stood over the artist while he prepared the drawing, ran it personally through the duplicating machine and arranged for the drawing and a description of man and car to be distributed immediately to all police units in the area. As Saarbruecken is on the French border, he also alerted the customs and border police, and for a time the crossing point was closed.

Not possessing the ability to be in more than one place at one time, he had not done all of this personally, but had assigned what he could not manage to Sergeant Freimann, who was short, plump, had slightly protruding front teeth and was capable of moving a great deal faster than anyone would have suspected to look at him.

As a result of all this activity, the entire area was swarming with police throughout the night, every grey Opel Ascona was stopped and checked, and twenty-seven-year-old Hans Joachim Lauer was arrested as he was driving into Saarbruecken at a quarter to eight the next morning.

Lauer, a car mechanic, was on his way to work and

expressed great astonishment at his arrest. He had never, he protested, had any trouble with the police in his life.

This was quite true, but there was, none the less, a file on him at police headquarters as he had attempted suicide no less than four times, always apparently, with sincere intent, but, unfortunately, never with success.

He was also telling the truth when he said that he had never heard of Carmen Cojaniz and had no idea who she was.

He was less truthful when he said that he had not burned her alive.

Lauer matched the description given by Carmen Cojaniz to the last detail and, although he was not wearing them that day, the clothes that she had described were found in the wardrobe in the bedroom of the house which he occupied in the village of Bergweiler, not far to the north of Saarbruecken. His car was a grey Opel Ascona and it carried a Saarbruecken licence plate.

An identification by the victim was, of course, out of the question, although she was still alive at the time of Lauer's arrest. Even had she been able to stand the psychological shock of confronting her torturer, her eyes had been seared by the fire and she was blind.

The identification was not, however, necessary. The police were convinced that Lauer was their man and those who had seen the victim would probably have killed him and faced a murder charge rather than let him go free.

There was no need for such drastic measures either, for Lauer had not been very clever in his crime. At the time of his arrest, Carmen Cojaniz's clothing was still in the boot of his car.

Confronted with this irrefutable evidence, Lauer broke down and blamed the murder on his wife!

Her bullying, he said, and her threats of divorce fomented such a hatred of women in him that he had, accidentally and without intending any harm, set fire to a woman he picked up off the street because of her lovely breasts.

According to Lauer, his wife, Erika, who was the same age as himself, was very cruel to him. An employee in a Saarbruecken bank, she habitually drove the family car to work and he had to take the bus. The only reason that he had had the car that morning was that she did not work on Saturday and he did.

The inspector, who had seen Carmen not long after she was admitted to the hospital and was now having a little trouble keeping his hands off the suspect, asked grimly if it was not true that he had also had the car the evening before.

Lauer said, yes, but that it had been an exception.

Another of Mrs Lauer's cruelties which made her responsible for the death of Carmen Cojaniz was that she allowed her husband only very modest pocket money.

Informed of Hans Joachim's accusations, Mrs Lauer replied that they had an eight-year-old daughter to support, and after the money had been taken out for Hans Joachim's hobbies, a modest amount of pocket money was all that was left.

These hobbies, it seemed, were the basis of all of the Lauer family's domestic discord. A fanatic devotee of leisure-time avocations, he was a hobbyist to end all hobbyists and, incredibly, his greatest obsession was exactly that which Carmen's husband practised professionally. It was painting.

And, precisely like Cojaniz, Lauer's favourite and, indeed, only model had been his wife.

For over five years, Erika Lauer had patiently posed in her pretty pink skin during practically every minute that her husband was not working or asleep, while he struggled happily but incompetently to transfer her likeness to canvas.

She then decided that she had had enough. Posing naked seven evenings a week and all day Sunday was not her idea of marriage.

243

Lauer wept and complained. He did not drink away his money like other men. He did not chase women like other men. He did not smoke. All he wanted was to paint and his wife would not let him.

Erika countered with other suggestions. For two months she dragged him to a dancing school, where he learned to dance passably well.

But he did not want to dance. He wanted to paint.

Erika tried bowling. Once a week, they went bowling together. Hans Joachim became reasonably competent.

But he took no pleasure in his strikes and spares. What Hans Joachim wanted was to paint.

In desperation, Erika cleaned out the family savings account and bought him a ham radio outfit. Her reasoning was that, if she could get him interested in something other than painting, no matter what, it might dilute his enthusiasm for hobbies in general.

The result was a disaster. Hans Joachim became wildly enthusiastic about ham radio, but it did not cut down on his painting. Now, he painted in the evenings and stayed up most of the night with the ham radio. His wife and his daughter could scarcely speak to him he was so busy.

By that fateful Friday of 30 June, Erika Lauer had not yet actually filed for divorce, but she was giving the matter some very serious thought. She had finally come to the conclusion that nothing would separate Hans Joachim from his beloved hobbies.

She was quite right. When the presiding judge asked Lauer what he planned to do while in prison, he answered immediately and unhesitatingly, 'I'm going to paint.'

He was not going to paint Erika. Sick with horror at what her husband had done, she hired a lawyer the day following his confession and indictment and was granted a divorce in record time, the court failing to agree with Lauer's contention that the murder was her fault.

As for Hans Joachim Lauer, he confessed to the crime

and, when he found that he could not blame his wife for it, altered his statement to claim that the whole affair had been accidental and, therefore, no murder at all.

He had, he told the court, had no intention in the world of picking up any woman, let alone harming one, when he went off to work that Friday morning, but then he saw Carmen waiting to cross the street and he was so overwhelmed by the beauty of her breasts that he felt an irresistible impulse to paint her.

'You must understand me,' he told the judge earnestly. 'I am a painter and the creative urge . . .'

'I understand the creative urge perfectly,' responded the judge. 'What I do not understand is what happened afterward.'

That had all been an accident, protested Lauer. He just happened to have the pistol in the glove compartment of the car. It was only by chance that there was a nylon rope in the boot. It was sheer hazard that there was a box of matches in his pocket.

'You have testified that you are a non-smoker, Mr Lauer,' said the judge. 'Why would you carry matches in your pockets?'

Actually, the matches had not been in Lauer's pocket. Carmen Cojaniz had testified that he deliberately returned to the car to get them.

Lauer was unable to reply.

Erika Lauer was then called as a witness for the prosecution. Looking straight through her former husband, who smiled and waved, she testified that she had driven the car on Thursday, the day before the murder, and that there had been no pistol in the glove compartment and no nylon rope in the boot. To the best of her knowledge, there never had been either the one or the other in the car or in the house.

The police had been unable to trace where Lauer bought the pistol, a Belgian Fabrique National 7.65, but a hardware shop assistant identified Lauer as the man who had bought a coil of nylon rope two days before the murder.

Lauer's response was that he had been given the pistol as a birthday present, although he could not remember from whom. The rope, he said, he had never seen before he opened the boot. The hardware shop employee was mistaken.

Whatever his other failings, Hans Joachim Lauer was certainly not a man to give up easily, but his persistence did him, perhaps, more harm than good. The court took his efforts to reduce his responsibility badly and, on 16 March 1979, sentenced him to life imprisonment, the maximum sentence possible under German law.

There was probably nothing that Lauer could have done to avoid the maximum sentence. The jury had heard the tape recordings of Carmen's pitiful broken voice recounting the unpredictable horror that had over-taken her on a sunny summer afternoon and they had seen the pictures of her hideously tortured body.

As one of the jurors later told a reporter, 'There was no discussion on the verdict. The only question was how we could be sure that he would never be released.'

It was a question that went unanswered. No one serves a life sentence in Germany today and Hans Joachim Lauer will not either.

In the meantime, he is getting in a great deal of painting practice.

18

ALWAYS PREPARED

At ten minutes past eleven in the evening of 19 September 1982, thirty-two-year-old Jean Levallois reported for work at the entrance of the Carte Blanche club. It was a Sunday, but Levallois worked on Sundays. The club was open seven days a week and twelve hours a day from 11 p.m. to 11 a.m.

Open was, perhaps, not exactly the right term. The Carte Blanche was a very private club and admission was by membership card only.

Nor was the obtaining of a membership card such an easy matter. Unlike some of the other 'private' clubs in the Le Carré entertainment district of Liège, the Belgian city on the Meuse river, the Carte Blanche was a serious establishment where many of the owners and managers of the other night-spots came to relax from their labours. Annette Rosen, the thirty-nine-year-old manageress, was well known for running a superior place.

And also for her caution. Liège is a city of over a quarter of a million inhabitants and Le Carré is a tough district. Things happen to people there, unpleasant things.

Annette knew all about those things. She had been working in Le Carré most of her life, first as a waitress and then, beginning in 1979, just at the time that she was getting a divorce from her husband, as manager of the Carte Blanche.

Like most people who have worked hard to achieve their success, Annette was extremely conscientious and almost painfully punctual. The club opened on the dot of eleven and it closed on the dot of eleven.

And, because of this, Jean Levallois, a very large young man with a crew-cut who served not only as bartender but also as bouncer if the occasion arose, was amazed when she failed to respond to his knock at ten minutes past the hour. He had worked for Annette for over two years and this was the very first time that she had not been at the club when he arrived.

Or had she not heard him?

It was possible. If she was far at the back behind the bar, she might not have noticed a light rap on the door. After all, there was the vestibule in between the outside door and the actual entrance to the club rooms.

Levallois knocked again, harder. It did not occur to him that Annette might be sick. From what he knew of her, she would have dragged herself to work with two broken legs.

There was still no response, but, to his sudden alarm, the door seemed to move slightly under his knuckles.

Levallois pushed it. It swung open! The door was not locked!

Obviously, something catastrophic had taken place. It was unthinkable that the door should not be locked. It was Annette's first act upon arriving and her last when leaving. Whether she was inside or out, the door was always locked. The door was not broken nor was the lock. It had been opened with a key, and only Annette had a key.

Tense with apprehension, the bartender pushed wide the door and entered.

The vestibule was small, a passage some eight feet wide and ten feet long with the outside entrance at one end and a flight of three steps leading up to swing doors with glass port-holes at the other. It was floored with large squares of alternating black and white tiles and lit by sconces on both walls.

The lights were on and, lying on the black-and-white

tiles was the body of Annette Rosen. She was totally naked and she lay on her back with arms and legs spread wide. Against the white skin of her body, the bruises stood out, blue-black, like some strange, abstract design. From chin to shoulders, her throat was purple-black and swollen and, above it, her normally attractive features were distorted in the hideous grimace of the victim of strangulation, the eyes wide and staring and an unbelievable length of tongue protruding from the open mouth.

For an instant, Levallois stood paralysed, the great muscles of his thick shoulders swelling in anger. Annette had been a good woman and a good boss. It would have been a pleasure to get his hands on whoever had done this.

But, of course, he or they had long since gone and there was no way of even knowing who it had been.

Levallois relaxed, stepped carefully round the corpse, pushed through the doors to the club proper and headed for the telephone behind the bar.

He did not stop to examine the body for signs of life. Its appearance alone was enough to convince anyone that there would be none.

'A little over twelve hours,' said Dr Guillaume Sondrier, the tall, slender, balding medical expert attached to the department of criminal investigations of the Liège police.

'About the time the club would have closed this morning,' commented Inspector Victor Lejeune, chief of the homicide unit on duty that morning. 'Obviously, one of the customers.'

'The last,' said his assistant, Detective Sergeant Pierre-Louis Trefle. He was a very handsome man, dark-haired and dark-eyed with a fine, carefully-trimmed moustache.

The inspector also had a moustache, but it was neither fine nor carefully-trimmed and hung in a heavy black curve over the corners of his mouth so that he looked like a villain in a Victorian tragedy.

'Looks like a sex motive,' he observed. 'But was it

really? It's a strange place and a strange choice of victim for a sex psychopath.'

The doctor pressed his index finger and thumb on either side of his thin, prominent nose. 'I'm not certain,' he said. 'There appears to be no trace of semen in the vagina and, although she's bruised everywhere else, there are none of the typical bruise marks on the insides of the thighs which we could expect if she had resisted rape.'

'She did resist,' said the inspector. 'Otherwise, why all the bruises?'

'But she seems to have undressed herself,' said the sergeant. 'You see how the clothes are all lying here in a little heap? They'd have been scattered if he'd pulled them off her.'

'Seems likely,' agreed the inspector. 'What's that over there against the wall?'

The sergeant bent down to look. 'It's a tube of something,' he said. 'I can't see what it says on it unless I touch it.'

'Don't do that,' said the inspector. 'We'll wait until the lab crew gets here. There could be prints.'

There were, however, no fingerprints on what turned out to be a tube of vaseline. Too much of the contents had been smeared over the outside and it was less than half full.

'Strange,' said the inspector. 'A tube of vaseline? It must have belonged to her. I don't know what use a sex criminal could have for a tube of vaseline.'

Although an experienced investigator, the inspector was oddly naïve in some respects, but he was soon enlightened by the results of the autopsy.

'The vaseline served as a lubricant for anal intercourse,' said Dr Sondrier, who had come over to the inspector's office to discuss his findings. 'Her rectum was smeared with it and there is a high concentration of acid phosphotase in the lower bowel. It's not proof of intercourse, but it's recognized as a product of the break-down of semen.'

'Didn't occur to me that she'd have been raped like that,' said the inspector uncomfortably, rubbing his prominent chin, blue-black with a twenty-four-hour growth of beard. He had hardly had time to eat and sleep since the murder, let alone shave. 'Was there enough interval between the murder and the autopsy for the semen to break down?'

'Just about,' said the doctor. 'It was twelve hours before the body was discovered and then there was quite a delay before the laboratory people released the body for transfer to the morgue. Did they find anything useful?'

'Well, the tube of vaseline,' said the inspector. 'I don't know how useful it is. You can buy the stuff anywhere. The cash register was cleaned out. Levallois says there would have been around nine thousand francs in change in it.'

'He's not a suspect?' said the doctor.

The inspector shook his head. 'We checked his where-abouts at the time of the murder. His girl friend picked him up at the club at around ten-thirty and they went off to have lunch with another couple. He's clear, and all of the other employees are women.'

'Looks like you'll have an interesting time of it,' commented the doctor, getting to his feet. 'Well, good luck.'

'We'll need it,' said the inspector gloomily.

He was, as a matter of fact, not very optimistic concerning the chances of an early solution to the murder, or even any solution at all. Annette Rosen had probably not known her murderer and there would have been no previous contacts between them to trace. There had been no murder weapon other than the killer's hands and fingerprints were a waste of time. The only object that could be connected with the crime, the tube of vaseline, bore none. Of the hundreds of others recovered, there was no way of knowing which, if any,

251

belonged to the murderer. The place was a night-club. It was normal that there would be fingerprints everywhere.

'What intrigues me,' said Sergeant Trefle, 'is why she undressed. The lab people agree. She took her clothes off herself.'

'She undressed because the fellow threatened her,' said the inspector impatiently. 'Why else?'

'No doubt,' said the sergeant, 'but what I mean is, why did she meekly undress herself and then put up a terrific fight? If she was going to resist, why didn't she resist while she had her clothes on?'

'Hmmm, I see what you're getting at,' said the inspector, hunting through his pockets and producing a very small, very black cigar, which he tucked into the corner of his mouth but did not light. 'Well, maybe it was because she thought she could save her life by submitting to rape and it was only when she realized what he had in mind that she started fighting.'

The sergeant looked slightly disappointed. He thought that he had, perhaps, hit upon something significant, but the inspector had easily explained away the mystery.

'I suppose you're right,' he said. 'Have you decided on a line of investigation yet?'

'Yes indeed,' said the inspector. 'Take as many people as you need and find out who was in the Carte Blanche on the night preceding the murder. It's a private club, so there's a membership list somewhere. Establish the whereabouts of every member for the time of the murder. One of them killed Annette Rosen.'

The sergeant was a little dismayed at this simple, apparently foolproof plan with which the inspector proposed to solve the case. He had expected something more complicated and difficult.

He did not realize that, privately, the inspector thought it would end up more difficult too. God knew how many current and former members of the Carte Blanche club there were or how easy it was to lay hands on a card if there was some good reason for getting one, such as raping and robbing the manageress.

Before hearing the results of the autopsy, the inspector had been inclined to think that the sexual aspects of the case were little more than a diversion to throw off the investigators. The prime motive would have been robbery.

Even after learning of the anal rape, he would still have thought so, but for one thing: the tube of vaseline. The murderer had come prepared. He had had the intention of raping Annette Rosen before he even entered the Carte Blanche.

This conclusion altered the direction of the investigation. What the sergeant was now instructed to search for were customers of the Carte Blanche who were known perverts. Anal intercourse might not be a very unusual sexual deviation, but anal rape was.

For a day or two, the sergeant made little progress. The district was not one in which a great deal of cooperation with the police could be expected. However, as the news of the murder became more widely known, matters speeded up and there were even volunteers coming in with bits of information which they thought might be useful. Annette had been popular and everyone in Le Carré had known her.

Even so, it was nearly the end of September before forty-one-year-old Maurice Labeau and thirty-six-year-old Paul Estry came to police headquarters and said that they had information which might have a bearing on the Annette Rosen murder.

Both men were managers of night-spots in Le Carré and both were members of the Carte Blanche club. They had been in the club on the morning of the murder and it seemed nearly certain that they had been the last people, aside from the murderer, to have seen Annette alive.

In their statements, Labeau and Estry said that they

had gone to the Carte Blanche at approximately eight o'clock on that morning after closing their own establishments. It was something that they did nearly every morning after finishing work.

The statement did not surprise the inspector. He was aware that night-club managers and owners often spend their free time in other night-clubs, just as restaurant owners and cooks often go to eat in other restaurants.

Normally, Labeau and Estry would have gone to the Carte Blanche alone, but, on that particular morning, they had had with them a customer from Labeau's establishment who had still not wanted to go home at eight in the morning. He had begged so piteously to be taken along that they introduced him into the Carte Blanche.

'Did he apply for a membership card?' said the inspector.

It was an important point. If the visitor had applied for membership, his name and address would be on the club membership list.

The man had not, it appeared, applied for membership, but came in simply as a guest of Labeau and Estry, both of whom Annette knew well.

They were, in fact, old personal friends and it was obvious the two men were now worried that their introduction of the stranger into the club was the direct cause of Annette's death.

'It was a stupid thing to do,' said Labeau. 'We didn't know the type from Adam. He was just a customer and he wasn't even a regular. I never saw him before in my life.'

'And he was still in the Carte Blanche when you left?' said the inspector.

'I thought he wasn't,' said Labeau. 'We were talking with Annette and Jean and, the next thing we knew, the guy was gone. I thought he'd left.'

'So did I,' said Estry. 'There were only the three of us in the place and then he wasn't there any more so I reckoned he must have left.'

254

'And you reckon now he didn't,' said the inspector. 'All right. What did he look like and what do you know about him?'

Neither Labeau nor Estry knew anything about the man. He was a customer who drank white wine and cognac, a potent mixture, but he had not, it seemed, drunk very much cognac.

On the description, they did better. The man was young, under thirty, clean-cut and good-looking. He was very big, six feet four inches tall or more and well-built. He was dressed in jeans and a checked shirt and he had the look of a working man about him. There was a large, crooked scar approximately two inches long on his left cheek. His eyes were brown and so was his short, not stylishly cut hair.

Labeau and Estry spent the remainder of the day with the police artist, who eventually produced a drawing which both described as a good likeness of the suspect, and that same evening the sergeant's men moved into Le Carré armed with copies of the picture. Unless Labeau and Estry had murdered Annette themselves, the man represented in the drawing was the murderer.

Labeau and Estry had, of course, immediately been investigated. The old ploy of coming to the police to report a murder you have committed yourself is still tried now and then.

It was not possible to clear them completely. After leaving the Carte Blanche, they had gone to still another bar where they were well known, and a number of witnesses had seen them. However, as the exact time of the murder and the exact time of their arrival at the other bar were not known, it was at least physically possible for one or the other of them to have committed the crime. It could not have been both. Annette had been raped by only one man.

Despite this possibility, neither man was ever considered a serious suspect. Estry had a police record

255

of one conviction, but it was for receiving stolen goods and not for a morals offence.

Although now armed with a drawing and description of a highly promising suspect, there was still no immediate progress, for the sergeant's detectives had a great many places to canvass. It was only on 3 October that they were able to pick up the trail.

On that date, the owner of a bar called Le Crocodile tentatively identified the drawing as being that of a man who had come rushing into his bar at a few minutes before noon on Sunday 19 September.

The man, a stranger who had never been in the bar before, appeared excited and out of breath. He went straight to the bathroom, where he washed his hands very thoroughly, coming out to ask the bar-owner for more soap. He then spent about an hour and a half in the bar, drinking beer and becoming involved in conversation with one of the regulars.

A team from the police laboratory promptly descended on the bar, took apart the plumbing of the lavatory and were eventually able to report traces of vaseline in the trap. It was, of course, no proof, but it was an indication.

In the meantime, the regular customer from Le Crocodile who had had a conversation with the stranger was located and brought to police headquarters, where he too described the drawing as being a good likeness of the suspect.

He had not learned the man's name or where he came from, but he had asked him about the scar and the man had said that it was the result of an automobile accident in Vottem when he was seventeen.

As it was not known how old the man was now, the year in which the accident had taken place could not be determined and, as there was no way of knowing whether the accident had even been reported to the police, an identification from traffic accident records was not feasible.

The mention of Vottem was, however, important. It

was one of the working-class suburbs to the north of the city and, although there was no evidence that the suspect lived there or even had lived there at the time of the accident, it provided another link in the chain, if there was a chain at all.

The sergeant and his detectives moved out of Le Carré and into Vottem and, almost immediately, they began to receive positive identifications of the artist's drawing.

By 7 October, the man's name and address were known. He was twenty-six-year-old Francesco Cuestra-Ortega, a Spanish citizen born in Malaga, who had come to Belgium at the age of ten with his parents and been there ever since.

Cuestra-Ortega, a house painter, had been unemployed for the past fourteen months. He was married and the father of a three-month-old daughter, who had been baptised just one week after the Annette Rosen murder. Had it not been for his police record, he might have seemed an improbable suspect.

According to the records, however, he had already been convicted twice of morals offences, once in 1978 and again earlier in 1982.

The cases were identical. The Spaniard had simply jumped on women from behind in the open street and attempted to rape them, hauling up their skirts and stripping down their panties for the purpose.

The women had, of course, screamed and fought, and people in the vicinity had come to their rescue, in both cases restraining Cuestra-Ortega until the police arrived.

As neither victim had been raped or had suffered any injury other than to her dignity, the would-be rapist had been given a stern lecture by the judge and sent off about his business.

'The man's bisexual,' said the inspector. 'The victims thought he was trying to rape them vaginally, but he wasn't. He was going to attack them in the same manner that he attacked Annette Rosen.'

'He's certainly mixed up sexually in some way,' said

the sergeant. 'Ninety per cent of the identifications of the drawing were from homosexual bars and night-spots. On the other hand, he's been married for three years and he's the father of a child.'

'Well, whatever he is, he's a murderer,' said the inspector. 'Bring him in and we'll see what we can do about getting a confession out of him.'

Not much, it turned out. Taken into custody and charged with the murder of Annette Rosen, Cuestra-Ortega stubbornly denied all connection with the crime. He had, he said, not gone out in months. He was a family man and a father. His place was in the home.

If he thought that his wife would support this statement and provide him with an alibi, he was mistaken.

Twenty-two-year-old Josephine Cuestra-Ortega had been married for a scant three years, but already the magic had gone out of her marriage.

'He's been out all night three and four nights a week ever since we got married,' she said coldly. 'As I remember it, he was out that Saturday night and Sunday morning too.'

She then went off to talk to an attorney about a divorce.

The attorney assured her that it would be a simple matter if her husband were to be indicted for homicide and, as that was precisely what happened, Mrs Cuestra-Ortega had no difficulty in dissolving her marriage.

Although her husband still refused to confess, he was indicted on charges of rape and murder on the basis of physical evidence and the testimony of witnesses.

Both Maurice Labeau and Paul Estry were successful in picking Cuestra-Ortega out of a line-up as the man who had accompanied them to the Carte Blanche club on the morning of the murder. Both testified they had not seen him leave the club and only assumed that he had gone because he was not in the room.

'Instead of leaving the club, he went and hid in the men's room until Labeau and Estry left,' said the inspector. 'He'd already made up his mind to rape Annette Rosen and all he had to do was wait until the others were gone.'

'He couldn't have gone there with that intention,' argued the sergeant. 'There's no evidence that he ever saw the victim before in his life. The manager could have been a male, heavyweight wrestling champion.'

'It wouldn't have made any difference,' said the inspector. 'He was armed with that old Bulldog revolver we found in his apartment and he was bisexual. The wrestler would have got the same treatment as Annette Rosen, although he wouldn't have been able to strangle him to death, perhaps. The man was always prepared.'

'Yes, I suppose you could say he was,' said the sergeant.

At the time of his arrest, Francesco Cuestra-Ortega had been carrying on him a tube of vaseline of the same brand as the one found at the scene of the crime, and a small stock of similar tubes was recovered from his home.

Confronted with the testimony of the two night-club managers, Cuestra-Ortega changed his story slightly. He admitted that he had been in the Carte Blanche club on that morning, but said that he had left almost immediately.

Labeau and Estry had been there when he left and it was, undoubtedly, they who had murdered Annette.

The police, he charged, knew this, but they were trying to pin the crime on him because of his past record and because he was a foreigner. Labeau and Estry were both Belgians.

This was a popular and stylish defence. Defendants everywhere have long since learned that accusations of police brutality are nearly as effective as claims of racial discrimination in arousing the sympathy of courts and media.

But not always. On 6 January 1984, a jury found Francesco Cuestra-Ortega guilty of rape and murder with no extenuating circumstances. He was sentenced to life imprisonment.

He will probably not serve it. The Belgian taxpayers already carry a heavy enough load without paying for the lifetime support of Spanish citizens.

On some fine morning not too far in the future, Francesco Cuestra-Ortega may, perhaps, be quietly escorted to the border and shoved across with an earnest recommendation not to set foot in Belgium again.

19

GETTING TO KNOW THE NEIGHBOURS

Despite the confused though purposeful sexual aspirations of Francesco Cuestra-Ortega and his handy tubes of vaseline, Latins, in general, are not as sex-obsessed as is widely believed in the northern latitudes. Many southern Europeans live in economically depressed areas and they tend to give more thought to getting something to eat than to sexual frolics.

This is, of course, not true for such prosperous places as Turin, the centre of the Italian car industry in which many of the city's more than a million inhabitants are employed.

However, even though prosperous and able to devote more thought and energy to the procreative pleasures, many of the residents of Turin still appear to prefer the wholesome, church and government sanctioned and approved variety.

This spiritual and administrative approval was fully shared by Mrs Teresa Ambruzzi, coming round on the morning of Sunday, 25 November 1979, to visit her daughter and her son-in-law of just over a month.

Mrs Ambruzzi not only approved of the marriage; she approved of her son-in-law. Twenty-seven-year-old Paolo Nardin was not rich, but he was handsome, hardworking and gainfully employed.

Equally important, Margherita unquestionably loved him. Privately, Mrs Ambruzzi had been becoming a trifle concerned. Margherita was, after all, twenty-three and,

261

although this was not Sicily, where she would have been practically an old woman, still . . .

Teresa Ambruzzi was, therefore, very happy as she climbed the stairs to the little apartment at 53 via Pascolo in the Turin suburb of Barta at approximately eleven o'clock that morning.

She would not remain in that state for long.

The fact that there was no immediate response to her knock did not alarm her. Margherita had told her earlier in the week that she and Paolo were entertaining another young married couple on Saturday evening, and she supposed they had got to bed late.

Mrs Ambruzzi knocked harder.

There was still no response.

Mrs Ambruzzi hammered on the door panels with her fists and cried out her daughter's name in piercing tones.

A sleep-drugged voice from the apartment next door protested, 'In the name of Christ, madam!'

Bewildered, Mrs Ambruzzi automatically tried the door handle.

The door was not locked!

Mrs Ambruzzi's emotions, which had gone from happiness to disappointment to bewilderment, abruptly changed to terror. There are few communities of over a million where people in their right minds go to bed with the door unlocked, and Turin was not one of them.

Her heart beginning to beat painfully hard, Mrs Ambruzzi pushed open the door and entered.

For an instant, she felt a sensation of relief. She had half expected to find her daughter and son-in-law trussed like turkeys and the apartment ransacked. There were, after all, the wedding presents.

However, the tiny entrance hall and the living room opening off it were in order and she could even see her own wedding gift, a fine silver coffee and tea service which had nearly bankrupted her, standing on the sideboard. There was no sign of Margherita and Paolo.

The feeling of foreboding returned tenfold. It would

have been far better had they actually been tied up in the living room. The combination of the appearance of normality in the apartment and the apparent absence of the occupants lent itself to the most frightful conjectures.

But not as frightful as reality. Crossing the living room on tip-toe as if she feared to awake someone or something, Teresa Abruzzi pushed open the door to the bedroom.

And crumpled to the floor as her knees gave way beneath her. The terrible premonitions which she had been experiencing since finding the door to the apartment unlocked were appallingly exceeded, and the shock struck her with all the force of a hammer blow.

After that, Teresa Abruzzi had only a vague concept of time. She was not certain how long she lay in a faint in the doorway of her daughter's bedroom, but, according to the hospital records, her telephone call for the ambulance was received at precisely eleven-thirty-seven.

Mrs Abruzzi had called the ambulance rather than the police because she was a mother and she could not accept that her beloved daughter was really dead, although she must have known it subconsciously, if nothing else.

The ambulance crew knew it almost as soon as they entered the bedroom, but they carried out a check for respiration and heartbeat on both corpses anyway.

There was none, of course, and both the bodies were cold and stiff with rigor mortis. The ambulance crew withdrew, leaving them undisturbed, and devoted their efforts to calming Mrs Abruzzi while they awaited the arrival of the police.

They were not long in coming, but the first unit to arrive was only a patrol car and the officers could do no more than confirm the report by the ambulance crew that a double homicide had taken place at 53 via Pascolo in Barta.

The duty homicide squad was, however, already on the way and, at a little after twelve, Inspector Luciano

Cavallo, Detective Sergeant Mario Brisetti and Dr Roberto Andreotti entered the bedroom of the little apartment.

The sight which met their eyes did not have the impact on the seasoned criminal investigators that it had had on Mrs Abruzzi, but, even though it was by no means the most gruesome murder scene they had ever encountered, it was exceptionally sickening simply by reason of the youth and beauty of the victims.

Paolo and Margherita Nardin had been unusually attractive young people and, even in death, they still were. Whatever expressions their faces had worn at the time of death, horror, fear, agony, they were now relaxed and peaceful.

Paolo lay on his back on the floor beside the bed, his right arm stretched out in the direction of Margherita as if he was still striving to reach her even in death.

He was fully dressed, but his clothing was disarranged as if he had been engaged in a scuffle. The front of his pale blue shirt was covered with an irregular dark-brown stain of dried blood and a thin trickle had run from each corner of his mouth. His eyes were closed.

On the bed, his wife lay totally naked in the classic position of the rape victim, her legs bent at the knee and tipped backward on either side. There were black bruise marks on her thighs and arms, but only a little blood had run from the narrow slit, scarcely half an inch long, between her breasts. It did not look like a serious wound.

'Switchblade,' said Dr Andreotti, tight-lipped. 'Touched the heart or a major blood-vessel. The bleeding was all internal.'

He was a tall man with an olive complexion, plump and well-groomed. His seemingly emotionless black eyes looked out of professional gold-rimmed glasses. The eyes were deceptive. The doctor was, in fact, almost too compassionate for the type of work he did, which did not, however, mean that he was not good at it.

'Time of death, around midnight last night,' he

264

continued. 'Cause, a single knife-wound in the chest in both cases. In all probability, the same knife. It was a switchblade, because a stiletto would have been double-edged and anything else would have left a wider cut.'

'She was raped, I suppose?' said the inspector, a short, dark, wiry man with a very heavy beard and black hair on the backs of his hands.

The doctor carried out an examination of the dead girl's genitals.

'Positive,' he said. 'She resisted so fiercely that he damaged her sex organs in effecting penetration, but he achieved his objective. There are definite traces of semen in the vagina.'

'Sex psychopath,' observed the sergeant. Like many northern Italians, he was blond, blue-eyed and looked as if he would be more at home in a German beer hall than an Italian police station. 'Should I get the records section started on pulling the known-sex-offender files?'

'Yes,' said the inspector, 'but first, let's see if we can arrive at a picture of what happened here. There may be some factors that the computer can make use of in establishing a profile.'

This was important because the profile was often the only means that the police had of identifying potential suspects in deviate sex crimes. Unlike crimes committed for other motives, there was often no previous contact between murderer and victim to be traced.

Later, the specialists from the police laboratory would attempt the same thing, but Inspector Cavallo preferred to make his own reconstruction independently.

'Midnight,' he mused. 'They were probably getting ready to go to bed. She was already undressed, because there are her clothes folded over the chair. He was still dressed. See if there's any sign of a forced entry, Mario.'

The inspector did not know that Mrs Abruzzi had found the door to the apartment unlocked. He had taken one look at her, judged her to be in no condition to make a statement and ordered the ambulance to take her to the hospital. The statement could be taken later.

The sergeant returned to report that there was no sign of a forced entry on the apartment door.

'All right,' pursued the inspector. 'He simply knocked at the door and the husband answered. How did they all end up in here?'

'He must have forced him into the bedroom with the knife,' said the sergeant, 'but I don't see how he could have raped and stabbed the wife without the husband jumping him. Both of them seem to have put up a fight.'

'And, considering the resistance the wife put up, she wouldn't have simply remained quietly in the bed while he was killing her husband,' said the doctor. 'At the least, she'd have screamed her head off.'

'Maybe the husband couldn't take any action because the killer had the knife at his wife's throat,' said the inspector.

'Then, how could she put up such resistance?' said the doctor. 'She wasn't coerced under threat of the knife and she was a young, strong woman. He'd have needed both hands to subdue her.'

There was a short silence during which could be heard the sound of the siren of the police van bringing the specialists and technicians to the scene.

'Then the only explanation is that they weren't both present when she was killed,' said the inspector finally. 'He was out of the apartment for some reason and the rapist came in and raped the wife. She resisted. He stabbed her. At that moment, the husband returned. There was a fight and he killed the husband too.'

'That means it was somebody who knew them,' said the sergeant. 'He'd have to be able to observe when the husband left and he'd have to know that there was a young woman alone in the apartment.'

'Sounds logical,' said the inspector. 'And, if that's what it was, it'll make our job easier.'

He was, of course, speaking comparatively. Obvi-

266

ously, the job was not going to be easy. The killer might have known who the victims were and something about them, but that did not necessarily mean that he had had any traceable contact to them. He had probably been in the apartment for no more than twenty minutes or half a hour, and he would have touched scarcely anything. Even if he had, any fingerprints recovered would be of value only if he had a police record. The murder weapon he had apparently taken with him.

But, according to the laboratory technicians, he had left something else behind. A white imitation-leather jacket with the word AMERICA printed across the back in scarlet letters which had been found lying on the floor near the bed.

'It didn't belong to Nardin,' said the chief technician, reporting to the inspector. 'It's two sizes too large.'

It was past four in the afternoon and, by now, the investigators knew the names of the victims and everything else that there was to know about them.

It was not much. Paolo and Margherita had been very average in every respect except physical appearance. Children of middle-class families, both had completed their secondary school education and Paolo held an adequate job in a storage and warehousing firm. They had been engaged for two years before marrying and they had not lived together during that time.

Natives of Turin and, indeed, Barta, they had had many friends, but the young couple with whom they spent the last evening of their lives had been located and were now engaged in making a tearful statement to Sergeant Brisetti. It was not believed that it would be of much value to the investigation.

Surprisingly, it was, for it solved one of the major mysteries in the case: why had Paolo Nardin left the apartment after the guests had departed?

Paolo, said the couple, had gone out to look for his motorbike. They had left at approximately midnight and

Paolo politely accompanied them down to the courtyard in front of the house, where he immediately noticed that his motorbike, which had been parked in front of the house when they arrived at around eight, was missing.

He assumed that it had been stolen and was very upset, but they reassured him, saying that it was probably just some kid from the neighbourhood who had pinched it for a ride and would abandon it when the petrol ran out.

Paolo appeared relieved, but said that he was going off to look for it immediately. There had not been much petrol in the tank and it should have run out by now.

The last they saw of him, he was setting off down the via Pascolo.

'And upstairs the door to the apartment was, of course, unlocked,' said the sergeant, 'because he hadn't expected to go anywhere. He was just coming back up.'

'Incredible!' muttered the inspector. 'Was the whole thing simply bad luck? The murderer just happened to hit on what was probably the only unlocked door in the whole building?'

'And behind that door, the prettiest young woman in the neighbourhood,' added the sergeant. 'I don't see how it could be chance.'

'Nor I,' said the inspector. 'He knew who was in that apartment and he knew that Nardin would go out and leave his wife alone because he arranged it. It was he who took away the motorbike. Get out a notice to all uniform units that we're looking for a motorbike. You should be able to get the licence number and description from the vehicle registry.'

'Right,' said the sergeant. 'We're also canvassing in the neighbourhood for anyone seen wearing a white imitation-leather jacket with the word AMERICA printed on it. How late do you want them to continue?'

'Until they get something,' said the inspector grimly. 'I'll be here at the station until they do.'

All that the inspector was going to learn that night

was that the findings of the autopsies carried out by Dr Andreotti confirmed precisely what he had said at the scene. Margherita had been raped and stabbed through the heart. Paolo had been stabbed through the heart and the left lung. The interval between the two deaths was so short that it was not possible to say which had died first. The weapon had been a switchblade.

'Keep working on the jacket and the bike,' said the inspector. 'I want results. The boy is too dangerous to leave running around loose.'

No trace of Paolo Nardin's stolen motorbike was found, but the following afternoon the sergeant came in with two potential witnesses in connection with the white jacket.

Both married women, aged respectively thirty-one and thirty-two, they requested that their identities not be revealed, not, it developed, out of modesty, but fear. The party concerned was insanely violent, they said, and, if word of their testimony were to get back to his ears, they would have to flee Turin, if not Italy.

On the afternoon of Saturday, 24 November, said the women, whose statements were made separately but agreed in every detail, they had been visiting a Mrs Maria de Ronzo, a twenty-nine-year-old housewife and the mother of two children aged seven and five.

They were old friends of Mrs de Ronzo, whom they had known prior to her marriage. They were not friends of her husband, forty-year-old Arturo de Ronzo, for whom they used the term 'monster'.

And, if their story was true, he certainly was. While they were chatting with Maria, a modest and respectable woman, her husband suddenly appeared in the doorway of the room and brusquely ordered her to come with him.

Maria reluctantly and fearfully obeyed and her husband took her to a table in the next room, bent her over it and, turning up her skirts, subjected her to what struck the visitors as extremely brutal intercourse. As de

Ronzo had not bothered to close the door, they had an unobstructed view of the proceedings.

De Ronzo then went off somewhere and Maria returned to continue the chat. The visitors did not, however, feel entirely at their ease and left after a short time.

Mr de Ronzo, said the witnesses, was wearing a white imitation-leather jacket with the inscription AMERICA in scarlet letters across the back.

'The de Ronzos live at 56 via Pascolo,' said the sergeant. 'It's directly across from the Nardin apartment building and they're one floor higher.'

'Well, I suppose that does it,' said the inspector. 'Unless the ladies are simply trying to settle a personal grudge against de Ronzo. Keep him under permanent surveillance and see what else you can learn about him in the neighbourhood. Does he have a record?'

De Ronzo did not, but, according to what the sergeant learned in the neighbourhood, he should have had. He was regarded as a sort of sex fiend by almost every woman who knew him and several reported that he had made unsuccessful attempts to rape them or their children. De Ronzo had apparently never heard of the generation gap and was prepared to rape victims of any age.

'And, if any more proof is needed,' said the sergeant, 'there are dozens of statements that he habitually wears a white imitation-leather jacket with the word AMERICA on it in red and he's not wearing it now.'

'Bring him in,' said the inspector shortly.

De Ronzo, a short but extremely muscular man with a scraggly beard, was taken into custody and charged with the murders of Margherita and Paolo Nardin.

He denied all knowledge of the crimes and, when confronted with the white imitation-leather jacket with the word AMERICA on the back, said that it did not belong to him, he had never seen it and he had never owned such a jacket.

When the statements of his neighbours were read to

him, he accused them of trying to get him into trouble. Everyone in the neighbourhood hated him, he said, because he was poor.

De Ronzo was, as a matter of fact, no poorer than some, but he was right about everyone hating him. Quarrelsome and violent, he was a feared bar-room fighter and even his own wife testified against him, saying that she had wanted to get a divorce for a long time, but had been afraid that her husband would kill her if she even mentioned it.

De Ronzo, she said, was obsessed with sex and had subjected her to every form of perversion that the human body could withstand. She was also certain that he had raped women in the neighbourhood who had not dared to report it to the police, for he had bragged to her about it. She knew nothing about the Nardin murders, but she did not doubt her husband capable of them and she did not know where he had been on the evening in question.

The inspector did, and when Paolo Nardin's motorbike was found hidden in de Ronzo's garage and a switchblade still bearing bloodstains was recovered from a sewer-opening behind his house, de Ronzo was forced to agree.

It was true that he had murdered the Nardins but it was not his fault. It was partly the fault of the Nardins themselves and partly the fault of the television programmes.

The announcer on one of the programmes that evening was altogether too sexy and she put him into a state.

Then, the Nardins were not careful about drawing their curtains when they undressed for bed and he had had the opportunity to observe Margherita on several occasions nude or partly nude. She was a very pretty woman and the television announcer made him think of her.

Looking across the street, he was able to see that the Nardins were entertaining, and he hit upon the idea of

271

luring Nardin away from the apartment by hiding his motorbike.

He thought that Nardin would go looking for it the moment he noticed it was gone, and he was right.

In the meantime, while Nardin was escorting the guests downstairs and going to look for his motorbike, Margherita went to the bedroom and undressed completely before climbing into bed to wait for Paolo.

He watched this from his own window and, the moment Paolo was out of sight, ran across the street and up the stairs to the Nardin apartment.

The door had not been locked and Margherita, hearing him enter, called out, 'Paolo? Hurry. I'm waiting for you.'

He went into the bedroom and took off his jacket as he thought it would interfere with what he had in mind.

Margherita, who did not know him as she and Paolo had only moved into the apartment a month earlier, was so amazed and indignant that she was not able to stammer out anything more than, 'Who are you? What are you doing here?' before he was upon her and had his hand over her mouth so that she could not scream.

Realizing then what he intended, she fought like a tigress and managed to scratch him slightly on the neck. Unable to keep his hand over her mouth and force her legs apart with the other, he lost patience, pulled out his switchblade and stabbed her.

She then, said de Ronzo with some satisfaction, lay still and there was no further problem.

Unfortunately, just as he was finishing his business, Nardin returned and flung himself upon him. There was a terrific battle, but he was stronger and more experienced in fighting and he soon gained the upper hand, pinning Nardin to the floor and driving the switchblade into his chest.

He was certain, now the police knew what had happened, they would agree that the murders had not been his fault. If Margherita had not made such a fuss and had held still for a minute, he would not have had to kill her. And, if Nardin had not attacked him, he would not have killed him either. It had been, basically, a case of legitimate self-defence.

The police did not agree. Nor did the court. On 5 September 1980, an indignant Arturo de Ronzo was found guilty of one count of rape with violence and two counts of murder with no extenuating circumstances.

To the relief of everyone in Barta, but, particularly, Mrs de Ronzo, he was sentenced to two terms of life imprisonment not to run concurrently.

20

THE ZOMBIES ARE COMING!

She had been a gentle woman and she looked it even in death.

Not unattractive either, despite her eighty-two years. Unlike many older women, she had not made the mistake of having her hair cut too short and it lay in thick, soft folds on the pillow beside her head, not snow-white, not grey, an in-between colour like mother-of-pearl but without the iridescence.

The cheeks were a little sunken of course. She had taken out her false teeth before going to bed and they lay in a tumbler of blue cleansing solution on the night table. Beside them were her gold-rimmed glasses, her handkerchief, her little tin of throat lozenges, all the modest equipment of an old woman settling down for the night in her own bed.

If the face above the mouth was peaceful, the rest was shocking. There was a livid bite mark on the chin and other bite marks on the breasts and thighs, obscenely exposed by the flannel nightgown bunched up around the neck. The imprints of the teeth could be plainly seen, human teeth.

'Miserable pervert!' said Inspector Walter Becker. 'Isn't there anything they'll stop at?'

His assistant did not reply. Sergeant of Detectives Max Grossmann was familiar with his chief's outbursts and knew that the question was rhetorical. Although in his forties and with close to twenty years of criminal investigation work behind him, the inspector never failed to be outraged and angered by murders of children or women of any age.

Fortunately, there were not all that many such murders in Weiden. The population of the city was only a little over fifty thousand and it lay well off the beaten track, not far from the Czech border in southern Germany. There was barely enough work to justify the nucleus homicide squad formed by the inspector and sergeant.

And, as a rule, the homicides required little or no investigation. Mostly they were domestic affairs with husband or wife rushing to the police station in an agony of contrition and guilt, crying out, 'I have killed Agnes!' or Ilse or Juergen or Gunter or whatever the case might be. Not real murders, the inspector called them, and, as a matter of fact, they were seldom so charged. In nearly all cases, the prosecutor would settle for manslaughter.

This was different. Mrs Martha Preiss had not been killed by her husband, because he had been dead for many years. She had been killed by some kind of a deviate or psychopath and he or, less likely, she was obviously not going to come in tearful repentance to confess to the crime.

'Well?' said the inspector impatiently. He had been waiting for nearly ten minutes while the Weiden coroner, an elderly, white-haired man, carried out a very deliberate examination of the corpse.

'She's been dead for about twelve hours,' said the coroner, startled into a rush of words. 'Strangülation. Manual. It didn't take much. She was very old and a little pressure on the arteries carrying blood to the brain . . . She didn't suffer much.'

'And the bites?' snarled the inspector. 'They didn't hurt?'

'Made after death, I think,' murmured the doctor. 'Otherwise, she would have thrashed around in the bed more.'

'Any suggestions as to the motive?' asked the sergeant.

'It wasn't sex in the normal sense,' said the doctor. 'There's no indication of attempted penetration. There are some spots here on the sheets and on her body too which I think may be semen. He probably masturbated over the corpse.'

'It's something,' said the inspector. 'Eliminates the possibility of a female suspect, at least.'

'And, I'm afraid, that's about all,' said the coroner apologetically. 'The laboratory technicians may find something or . . .?'

'Laboratory technicians!' snorted the inspector. He had little confidence in the four members of the Weiden police laboratory, who were, none the less, highly trained and competent. 'All right, Max. Tell them to come on over and you stay here to keep an eye on them. I'm going to take a statement from Mrs Tauchmann.'

It was fifty-one-year-old Rosa Tauchmann who had discovered her mother's body when she came to visit her on that Saturday morning of 3 March 1984. She immediately called the police and waited at the apartment at 11 Geiers Way until they arrived.

The inspector promptly sent her home in a patrol car, after having checked her identity and noted her address. She was obviously very badly shaken and there was no point in having her waiting at the scene until the doctor had finished with his preliminary examination of the corpse and the inspector had time to take her statement.

He had not thought that her statement would be of much value to the investigation and it was not. She had simply dropped in to see her mother, as she often did, and found her murdered. She searched for a pulse or any other sign of life and, finding none, called the police rather than a doctor or the ambulance.

'Would your mother have let a stranger into the apartment?' said the inspector.

'Never,' said Mrs Tauchmann. 'She read the newspapers and she watched television. She knew how safe an old person is today!'

276

'The door was locked when you arrived?' said the inspector. 'Do you have a key?'

'The door was locked,' said Mrs Tauchmann. 'I let myself in when she didn't answer the doorbell. I thought she was probably still in bed and didn't feel like getting up.'

'A silly question, perhaps, but I have to ask it,' said the inspector. 'Did she have enemies?'

'Very silly,' said Mrs Tauchmann. 'At eighty-two? Of course she had no enemies. Besides, even I could see it was some kind of a sex pervert.'

'There is such a thing as a faked sex crime,' said the inspector.

This one had not been faked. The spots on the sheets and on Mrs Preiss's body were semen and the bites were deep wounds and not token attempts to throw off the investigation.

The laboratory technicians had obtained excellent casts of the bite wounds. The marks of the teeth were so plain that they were confident of being able to identify a suspect by his teeth, should a suspect turn up.

So far, none had and, as the laboratory men had found nothing else at the scene and the search of the police records had turned up no previous cases of an offender biting the victim, the inspector was at something of a loss.

He had personally examined the door to the apartment and come to the conclusion that there was no way that the murderer could have entered other than with a key or through being let in by Mrs Preiss herself. He could, however, have gone out locking the door behind him as it was a Yale-type lock which snapped shut automatically when the door was closed. The only fingerprints on it were those of the victim.

He had had Sergeant Grossmann run a discreet check on Mrs Preiss's financial circumstances and the identity of her heirs.

Mrs Tauchmann was her sole heir, but she would

scarcely receive enough to cover the funeral expenses. Aside from her pension, Mrs Preiss had not possessed very much.

The case was, therefore, just what it seemed: a random murder by a psychopath whose only motive for the crime was the malfunctioning of his own mind. The sole mystery was why Mrs Preiss had let him into her apartment.

The inspector thought that, if that question could be answered, so too, perhaps, could be the other, more vital question of the identity of the psychopath.

It was highly unlikely that a woman of Mrs Preiss's age would have let a stranger into the apartment, particularly when she was already in her nightdress and either in bed or preparing to go there, simply because she found him attractive.

She had let him into the apartment because she knew him or had some compelling reason to believe that it was safe to do so.

If she knew him, however, that meant that someone within her circle of friends, relatives and acquaintances was a dangerous psychopath, and the inspector had been unable to find anyone among her contacts who had a record of mental illness.

This apparent contradiction troubled the inspector, a heavy-shouldered man with a broad forehead, a pronounced jaw and a black moustache like a broad bar across his upper lip, and it made him bad-tempered so that he growled at the other members of his family.

'Why do you watch such stupid junk?' he demanded of his fourteen-year-old son, who was watching with interest the forcible extraction of a pair of eyeballs in a video classic entitled *A Zombie Hung on the Bellrope*.

'What should I watch?' replied the young man. 'We don't have Little Red Ridinghood on the video.'

The inspector suppressed an impulse to kick his own flesh and blood and was about to pass on when he suddenly halted.

'Anybody get bitten in these things?' he barked.

It had just occurred to him the reason Mrs Preiss had let a stranger into her apartment might be that he had appeared so young she thought him harmless. At fourteen, the inspector's son was young enough to look like a boy, but strong enough to strangle an old woman.

Not, of course, that he suspected his own son in the crime, but all over the city other teenagers were watching horror films on television and in the movies, and there had been cases of attempts to translate into reality what they had seen. Less than three months earlier, a twelve-year-old girl had been gang-raped by her brother and four of his friends, who said that they had got the idea from a video film.

His question startled his son, who was not afraid of his father but, like many adolescents, sometimes feared for his sanity.

'Well, sure, yeah, Dad,' he said soothingly. 'People get bitten all the time. Vampires just about always bite the girls and zombies . . . This film here, for example . . .'

'Let's see it,' said the inspector. 'Let's see where the zombie bites the girl. Is it always a girl? Not an old woman?'

His offspring gave a guffaw. 'Who'd want to bite an old woman?' he chortled, and then, seeing the expression on his father's face, hurriedly ran the video cassette back to the last biting episode.

The inspector gave his son no reason to alter his opinion, watching the biting of the largely naked young actress in silence and then inquiring if there were any more such incidents in the film.

There were, and the inspector watched all of them as silently and as attentively. Zombies, it seemed, did little other than bite astoundingly well-built and mostly blonde young girls after tearing off their clothing.

The showing over, he absently thanked his son and departed, leaving the boy deeply concerned over the question of who would pay for his schooling once his father had been locked up in some institution for the incurably insane.

He would have been even more concerned had he known that the inspector himself was entertaining some doubts on the subject of his own sanity. For no logical reason, he became obsessed with the idea that Martha Preiss had been murdered by a zombie.

Not a real zombie, of course. The inspector did not believe that real zombies existed. But there were young, impressionable people who saw far too many horror and sex films, and one of them could have got the idea that he was a zombie and acted accordingly.

He tried to explain it to the sergeant, cautiously.

'Uh . . . that is, Max . . . what I mean is . . . uh, what do you think about zombies?' he asked diffidently when he and the sergeant were closeted in his private office with the door closed.

The sergeant, blond, blue-eyed and looking even younger than he was, stared at him for a moment without replying, his forehead slightly wrinkled.

'You're thinking of the Preiss case,' he exclaimed triumphantly, his face clearing.

The inspector admitted that he was.

'And horror films,' said the sergeant shrewdly. 'It's possible. The screens are full of it. It could be that somebody not entirely normal . . .'

'. . . was tipped over the edge,' finished the inspector. 'That's exactly what I've been thinking. The trouble is . . .'

'. . . it could be anybody,' said the sergeant, finishing the inspector's sentence in his turn.

'Well, no,' said the inspector. 'It would have to be either somebody she knew or somebody so young she didn't consider him dangerous.'

'So a limited number of suspects,' said the sergeant. 'If your theory is correct, we could solve it.'

The general opinion in the department of criminal

investigations had been that the murder would not be solved.

'The trouble, as I was saying,' said the inspector, 'is that we have no way of knowing who among the potential suspects might have gone over the edge. He may have no record of mental illness at all.'

'But he would be a horror-film fan,' said the sergeant. 'We could check how keen a potential suspect was on horror films. It would almost surely be video. The really rough stuff doesn't come on television or in the cinema.'

'The whole idea is fantastic,' said the inspector, 'but . . .'

'I'll start working up a list of every male she would have known well enough to let into the apartment,' said the sergeant. 'We already had one when we checked for mental cases among her contacts.'

'Don't forget the kids,' said the inspector. 'A woman that old and frail, a ten-year-old could have done it.'

Somewhat to everyone's relief, Mrs Preiss had known no ten-year-olds, not even casually, nor had she known any adolescents other than one boy who sometimes delivered groceries. He was quickly cleared. The autopsy had shown that Mrs Preiss died between eleven and midnight on 2 March, and the boy had a verifiable alibi for that time.

In the end, the list turned out to be shorter than had been expected. Mrs Preiss had had few friends. Like many older people, her friends were for the most part dead or in nursing homes and she had had little opportunity or inclination to make new ones. Outside the members of her family, a few delivery and service people and some of the other tenants in the same apartment building, she had known no one well enough to admit them into her apartment when she was in her nightgown.

'It must be one of the neighbours,' said the sergeant. 'We can place almost all of her relatives at the time of the crime and, anyway, they'd have had to come all the way across town to do it. I just can't see that. If they were nutty enough to do such a thing at all, they'd have picked somebody more convenient.'

'The delivery or public utilities people?' said the inspector. 'There was a mad meter-reader in Berlin a couple of years ago. Killed three or four old persons for their savings. They let him in because he had official identification as a meter-reader.'

'But he came round during the day surely,' said the sergeant. 'A man wanting to read the meter at eleven o'clock at night would rouse suspicion in anybody, and Mrs Preiss was known to be cautious.'

'All right,' said the inspector. 'The neighbours. How many are there?'

'Twenty-three, male,' said the sergeant. 'We've eliminated four who were demonstrably out of the building that evening, and two others are so old that they can't be considered valid suspects.'

'You're sure of that?' said the inspector.

'They haven't any teeth,' said the sergeant. 'Those bites weren't made with a set of dentures.'

'Hmmm, yes,' said the inspector. 'I wonder if we could take teeth prints of the other seventeen and . . .?'

'I asked the examining judge,' said the sergeant. 'He said only if they accepted voluntarily.'

'Then see how many will,' said the inspector. 'At the worst, we'll cut down the suspect list a little.'

The operation cut down the suspect list a great deal. Only seven of the tenants of the building where Martha Preiss had been murdered refused to permit casts of their teeth to be taken. The others were all cleared as their teeth did not match the bites on the victim's body.

'Excellent!' said the inspector, rubbing his hands together. 'We're closing in on him. Concentrate on those seven. If the theory is correct, he's among them.'

'If the theory's correct,' said the sergeant. 'As a matter of fact, we're already concentrating on one. He owns a video player and he's supposed to have the biggest collection of hard-core sex and violence films in Weiden.'

'Which would really be saying something,' said the inspector. 'What's his name and what is he?'

'He's nothing,' said the sergeant. 'That is, he's not studying and he's not working either. Nineteen years old. His name's Gerhard Beissel and he lives with his parents on the floor below Mrs Preiss's apartment.'

'Well, why don't you bring him in then?' said the inspector.

'We've got nothing against him,' said the sergeant. 'It's not illegal to collect porno and horror films.'

'It's illegal to murder old ladies,' said the inspector. 'Bring him in anyway.'

A man with old-fashioned ideas, he had never adjusted to the socialist principle of granting priority to the rights of the accused over those of the victims and the public.

The sergeant reluctantly took Gerhard Beissel into custody. He knew very well what would happen because it had happened before. The parents would get a lawyer who would arrange Beissel's release within a matter of hours, and the inspector would get another chewing-out by the examining judge who was ultimately responsible for the case.

And that was precisely what happened, but, before the lawyer was able to pry his client out of the inspector's clutches, there was a new development.

A young couple living on the same floor as Beissel came in voluntarily to the police station with information that they had apparently been withholding on the murder.

The couple, Peter and Karin Huber, both in their late twenties, said that they had heard of the arrest of Gerhard Beissel and that he was a friend of theirs. They did not believe him guilty and had come to tell the police of their mistake.

'Well?' said the inspector, scowling ferociously. He was quite certain that the Hubers were now going to provide Beissel with an alibi for the evening in question and he felt equally certain that it was false. However, even if it was, it would force him to release Beissel immediately.

To his surprise, the Hubers offered no such alibi, but began to hem and haw around and finally said that they thought someone else might have done it.

'Why?' demanded the inspector in a voice that sounded as if his vocal cords were made of brass.

'Well,' said Huber, 'the day after the murder, I mentioned it to Anton and he said, "So who cares? Another old bat out of the way." That was pretty callous.'

'Yes, indeed,' said the inspector, puzzled but gradually becoming interested. 'Is that all? Who is Anton?'

Anton, it seemed, was Anton Bleimeier, a journeyman baker who lived in the same building.

'We checked him out,' said the sergeant in response to the inspector's inquiring look. 'One of the seven who wouldn't let us take a bite cast, but nothing else. Not known to be a porno fan.'

'Not porno,' said Peter Huber. 'Horror. He's nuts about horror. Zombies in particular.'

'How do you know?' said the inspector. 'Is he a friend of yours too?'

Huber said, not exactly, but that Bleimeier often came to watch horror films on their video set. He did not own one of his own.

'He was with us on the evening of the murder,' he said, finally getting round to what he had come to the police to report. 'We watched *A Zombie Hung on the Bellrope*. He was like he was out of his mind with excitement. When the film was over, he jumped up and started hopping around the room on one leg, yelling, "I'm a little zombie too! I'll get all of you!" He scared Karin, so I told him he'd better leave – and he did. It was just about eleven o'clock.'

'Get some official witnesses and have this statement

sworn to and on tape,' said the inspector to Sergeant Grossmann. 'What does this zombie look like? Have I seen him?'

The inspector had not, but, even if he had, he would scarcely have taken Anton Bleimeier for even an imitation zombie. Thirty-two years old and considerably overweight, he had a clean-shaven, vacuous sort of face and a pear-shaped head with dark hair cut high over his ears and parted on one side. He was more flabby than muscular and he did not look dangerous.

Brought to police headquarters and accused of the murder, he protested his innocence at the top of his lungs and refused to answer any questions until he was represented by an attorney.

The attorney was produced, but the inspector, now convinced that he finally had the right man, possibly because he had seen parts of the film in question himself, demanded and received a court order to take a cast of Bleimeier's teeth with or without his approval.

It was without, and for good reason. The cast fitted the bite-mark casts taken from Martha Preiss's body perfectly. The case was solved. The murderer was a zombie.

Or, at least, an ex-zombie. Following his indictment for the murder of Martha Preiss, Bleimeier decided that he was not a zombie and never had been one.

Instead, he said he was an unfortunate, underprivileged person who had never had any breaks in his life and this had so warped his character that he had, more or less accidentally, killed Mrs Preiss, whom he knew only casually as a neighbour.

After the viewing of *A Zombie Hung on the Bellrope* he had been in a terrible state of excitement and he went to ring Mrs Preiss's doorbell simply because he knew that she was a woman living alone.

When she opened the door on the chain lock and saw that it was a neighbour, she let him in.

He rushed straight at her, dragged her into the

bedroom, strangled her on the bed and bit her in several places. It was, he said, what zombies did.

'If I am not mistaken,' said the inspector gravely, 'zombies generally rape their victims as well. Is that what you had in mind?'

He was trying to establish a motive that would make sense to a jury.

Oh no, said Bleimeier. He had had no such thing in mind. As a matter of fact, he couldn't rape anybody. He had never had contact with a woman in his life.

Rather incredibly, this was true, according to the psychiatrists who later examined him. At the age of thirty-two, in a society permissive enough to make Sodom and Gomorrah look like a Sunday school picnic, Anton Bleimeier was an intact virgin.

And, said the psychiatrists, likely to remain one. A latent homosexual, he was so confused sexually that he was probably incapable of intercourse with either sex, even if he remained at liberty.

Which he did not, although there was a good deal to his claim of being mistreated by society. He had been abandoned by his parents at the age of three, had grown up in an institution for homeless children, had never had any contact to a woman and had never had a friend of either sex. The court decided that they could not permit zombies to mingle freely with the public and, on 5 November 1984, sentenced him to life imprisonment.

Unfortunately, two of the judges at the trial had dozed off, an indication, perhaps, of the lack of interest which even a zombie can arouse in modern society, and the defence, noting this, moved for a mistrial.

A new date was set, but it did not help and, on 8 March 1985, the judges having managed to stay awake, another jury came to an identical conclusion and an identical sentence was handed down.